Karen Jennings

Travels with My Father
An Autobiographical Novel

Holland Park Press London

Published by Holland Park Press 2016

First Edition

ISBN 978-1-907320-69-9

Cover designed by Reactive Graphics

Printed and bound by

CPI Group (UK) Ltd, Croydon CR0 4YY

www.hollandparkpress.co.uk

Travels with My Father is a beautifully written autobiographical novel. Written from the point of view of a young woman, daughter and writer, it is a frank, yet delicate and moving, account of her relationship with her father and his influence on her own life.

In the footsteps of her father, the author travels the world. Yet, key scenes are set in Plumstead, a suburb of Cape Town, where her father lived most of his life.

The relationships and divisions between members of a family that does not wear its heart on its sleeve, and some of whom are real eccentrics, are sensitively recorded. It all adds to an intricate picture of a changing South African society.

PART ONE: PRESENTING THE DEAD

THE BIG HOUSE

Six months after my father's death, I fall in love. I am 29 years old and have been in love before, yet this time I am caught off guard. In the past months I have been mostly alone, staying in the house with my mother, reluctant to go out, especially at night. The house is large and we use separate lounges and bathrooms, eat at different times. Even so, the house feels small, my life outside the house even smaller. I am teaching history part-time at the same school where my mother teaches Afrikaans. I have only two classes – less than two hours a day. I accepted the position so that I could spend most of the day caring for my father, but he passed away two weeks into the first term. So my mother and I work together, live together. We shop together, go to movies together. We are dependent on one another, though we tell others that we are careful not to be. I don't like to leave her at home alone, but at times I am anxious to get out and away.

I tell myself that I will use the time to write. I pretend that I am, but I write nothing. I pile books on my bedside table that I plan to read. I don't even open them. I am not certain of what grief should be. Is it this? My mother's grief is more manifest. She has grown confused and forgetful. She walks slower than before. Repeats herself. Leaves doors unlocked and can't remember how the computer works. I hate her for this. I have no patience and we argue daily. Perhaps this is how I grieve; with anger and intolerance.

I meet Juliano accidentally. It is a Friday night and I am at a bar with acquaintances. I have not been out in months. It is cold and rainy and I did not want to leave the house. Under my jacket and scarf I am wearing a pyjama top. I turn around to go to the bathroom and I bump into him. We both apologise. I am surprised by his accent and he tells me he is from Brazil. We talk for the rest of the night. The first few weeks with Juliano I cry a lot. I cry every day, sometimes for hours. I feel like a fool.

He tells me that he understands, though I don't think he really does. But he is kind and thoughtful and when I cry he doesn't try to stop me.

As with all who fall in love, we do not like being apart and after a couple of months he asks me to move in with him. He lives in a loft apartment two kilometres away. I agree, but feel guilty. My mother is afraid on her own in the big house. I tell her that I will move out slowly, little by little. I will visit her every day. The distance is nothing. 'Of course,' she says, 'of course,' but she is upset. This is the house that she and my father bought shortly after their marriage. The house that they fixed up, made additions to, where they tended a garden and a swimming pool. The house that they raised their children in. Yet she has grown to despise the thing. The stretches of lawn and the pool that keeps turning green. The large rooms that gather dust. There are too many lounges, too many empty spaces. Too many places through which a burglar could enter. It is an old house. It needs attention and time and energy. She doesn't want to be there anymore. Not on her own. She begins to mention the possibility of selling and talks to a couple of estate agents, though my sister and I doubt anything will come of it. She is too indecisive lately.

Even before the house is on the market she begins to panic about clutter. She opens drawers and cupboards and despairs about the things we have amassed. The garage is full of boxes of objects that my father kept – our toys, our books, old tables, chairs, planks of wood, half-empty tins of paint. In the breakfast room are two small cake plates that my father brought home one day for my sister and I. I was perhaps five or six. I don't know where he got them. They are identical. A light blue base with a floral border, gold rimmed. He told us that we would hang them on the wall as decoration until we were old enough to have our own houses. Nobody seems to remember that I would sit in the breakfast room looking at them. I was trying to identify differences in the two plates, determining which was the best so that when it came to the point when my sister and I had to choose whose was whose, I would have the upper hand. When friends visited, I would point out the plates to them. As my mother de-clutters, she gives the plates away to her sister-in-law. I am torn apart. My mother and I scream at one another and do not talk for several days. But she gets the plates back without any difficulty. My sister doesn't want hers. She doesn't even remember him giving them to us. I take both to Juliano's flat where I display them on stands.

A month later the big house is for sale. I make a list of everything that must be kept. I want to avoid another misunderstanding or argument. The list is long. My mother and I fight again. We begrudge one another personal memories and want ours only. We have been living too long inside one another's grief. My father is, for each of us, ours alone.

THE LIST

The list of things to be kept includes, but is not limited to, the following:

A carved rosewood table that was brought to South Africa by one of the 1820 settlers
Two armchairs that belonged to my father's mother
Three pocket watches
An old Singer sewing machine table
A portrait of the Prince of Orange
The Children's Treasure House: 10 volumes
One captain's chair
Two small display cases
A silver cup
A silver candle holder
Pipe and hat ceramic ashtray
Shilling Herb Beer ceramic bottle
Golden hand-bell
Faux Chinese vase
Corner cupboard
Bookcases made by my dad
All the books in the bookcases except for the crime fiction
Two paintings, both in shades of blue: one of a workers' cottage in the veld, the other of people walking to *nagmaal* by moonlight
A porcelain jug
An old school hand-bell that is cracked on one side
Carved stone head book-end
Grandfather clock made by my mother's father
Oil lamp
Kist/tool chest
Riempie chair made by my mother's father
Magnet bearing the Jennings family crest
Any notebooks/notes/scribblings made by my father

Photo albums
An album full of postcards
The shirt I bought my father for Father's Day after his
surgery
The brown leather box in which he kept every one of the
teeth my sister and I lost as children
His comb
The pen he kept in his shirt pocket

Later, instead of fighting, my mother and I go through the house
together. We are like the blind – touching each object in order to
identify it and determine whether we want it or not. The process
is slow. We move forward in instalments.

I am in the process of moving in. Juliano had only a couch, a bed and a TV when I met him. Now I have stamped my mark with the pink armchair that I inherited from Great Aunty Kathleen along with a matching dressing table and stool, bedside tables and a small replica of a statue of a Roman charioteer (these I have left at the big house). The armchair is uncomfortable, ugly. I have no recollection of where it might have stood in her house. Even now the smell of old dog lifts from its bottom-frill on hot days. A reminder of the red-eyed, toothless spaniel that was all the companion Aunty Kathleen had after her son, her daughter, and finally her husband passed away.

The armchair is temporary; until I can afford something better. For the moment its use is to fill up space. Juliano drapes his clothes on it. I rest my handbag on it. Only sometimes, like now, do I sit in it. I have turned it so that I can look out across the balcony and see the street below. A bald man on his cell phone crosses the road between moving cars. Nearby a man on a bicycle has paused to roll a cigarette. A woman calls to him loudly, asking first the time, then how he is. They talk at full volume for a while before parting. I do not think they know one another. Minibus taxis come and go. There is no quiet in this road that stretches from beyond Cape Point all the way to the city centre with its five-pronged castle and high-rise buildings. Nearby houses have been turned into veterinary surgeries, cluttered second-hand stores, a place where eyelash extensions are done. A police station sits on a corner, its officials leaving their desks regularly to buy Cokes and packets of crisps at the café opposite.

To the left of the flat, beside a set of traffic lights, is an old building that advertises horse-race betting and slot machines. It was once the Diep River Hotel, where my grandmother's father, George Scaife, worked as the manager. The family lived in four rooms on the second floor of the hotel, where George later died.

A side road, almost directly across from the flat, leads to the hospital where my father died. Three women in nurses' uniforms approach the main road from the direction of the hospital. They hail a minibus taxi, laugh at something the *guardjie* says, and climb in heavily. The taxi drives off, cutting in front of traffic. It leaves in its wake a view of a girl in the side road sitting on the pavement. She is perhaps 11 or 12. She wears jeans and a T-shirt. Five minutes ago I saw her kicking a ball with a younger boy, her brother most likely. Now he sits on the opposite pavement, his position mirroring that of his sister. She is frowning, her arms are crossed. Still sitting, he kicks the ball at her. She picks it up and runs towards him. Her mouth is open; the faint sound of a shout reaches me where I sit. She runs past her brother, her mouth still open, throwing the ball over a chain-link fence into a field.

In fact, it is not so much a field as a plot of land, which flanks the gloomy Three Arts – a crumbling building which has in turn been used as a cinema, a theatre, a venue for music concerts, and for a short time a rat-infested ice-skating rink where a boy named Kyle once held my hand and guessed the date of my birthday. Finally, half-heartedly, as though aware of its inevitable failure, it existed briefly as a nursery. The relics of plants battle there untended now. Short palms and ferns persist in front of a building that longs to disintegrate and be forgotten.

Beyond the Three Arts are retirement villages, then, though I can't see it from here, the hospital. There is nothing significant about it. It smells the way hospitals smell. Looks the way hospitals look, with long corridors and doors that open and shut silently. In fact, during the delirium of his last days my father often thought himself in other hospitals. The army hospital he spent three months in when, at the age of 17, he broke his leg during compulsory army training. The state hospital on Alphen Hill where his mother died. The hospital in Kenilworth where I was born and where three years before his death my father had surgery to remove the cancer in his bowel.

Beyond the hospital, the land sinks and rises towards the mountains. Low on the slopes are vineyards, pine forests. It would be easy to forget the street, to focus only on the mountain that stretches boldly across a sky flecked with clouds. To think only of the vast and abiding rock that fences in the view on all sides. But the street, the hospital, people and traffic, and all the monotonous activity of a place living and dying, cannot be forgotten. It endures too, an indestructible thing that swells and shrinks without end.

There is an art involved in the presentation of the recently deceased. Props are used in order to give the dead an air of slumber. The body is cleaned, the face composed and a towel placed under the chin to prevent the jaw from hanging. An hour after my father's death, having prepared him for viewing, the nurses allow us to see him again.

Months afterwards I am driving to the flat; the boot of my car holds books, four dinner plates and a large ceramic umbrella stand imprinted with one of Alphonse Mucha's Moët & Chandon advertisements. I am not concentrating on where I am driving, simply on the process. I keep a careful eye on the distance between my car and the next. I am particular about putting on my indicator timeously, and about the sharp turn that the steering wheel requires as I drive into Burnham Road. I pause at the pedestrian crossing as a homeless couple push their Checkers trolley of belongings across into the Post Office parking lot. They make a living here, directing cars in and out of the ten or so parking spaces for a rand or two at a time. Next to them a woman sells flowers from a watering trough that has been here since at least the nineteenth century. Burnham Road is long, with several dips and rises. People often speed along this road, but I am careful to go below the speed limit. Again I switch on my indicator, turning the steering wheel left. I have parked my car and am pulling up the handbrake before I realise what I have done. I am in the hospital parking lot, parked in the same spot that I tried to use for most of the visits I made to my father during his last six days. I have not planned to come here, but I go inside anyway, careful not to try and justify it to myself.

Once I am through the automatic doors, I retrace my steps to the ward where my father had been. The same nurse who was on duty when my father died is behind the desk. She smiles at me and asks if she can help. I make no mention of my father or my connection to her and the hospital. Instead I tell her that I am interested in becoming a nurse and I would like to ask her a few questions. None come to mind. I mumble and stutter, eventually asking her about the difficulties involved in being surrounded by the dying. She tells me that the tidying of the body is her favourite part of the job. 'I get to be creative,' she says. 'The rest of the time it's just work work work, but when someone dies I can make them look nice again. I am good at it. I spend a long time just looking at the person's face and thinking about how they looked when they were alive. It's a gift that I get to give to the people who are left behind. Children, you know, and husbands and wives.'

When I say goodbye, we shake hands. Hers are rough, like a labourer or miner's, not like an artist's at all.

We stand in a row beside my father's hospital bed. Chemotherapy has reduced his hair to a fine fluff on the sides of his head. His skin is pale, his cheeks sunken. His beard has changed colour over the preceding months and is by now almost fully white. It is the first dead person I have seen, and perhaps I focus more on that than I do on the fact that this is my father laid out before me. I recognise him not as my father, simply as the body of the man that he has become over the past year.

'He looks like Lenin,' my mother says.

Two years previously, when my father had recovered enough from the surgery that had removed the cancer in his colon and had re-learned to defecate and digest, he resolved that it was time to pursue his lifelong dream of visiting Russia. He was not a well man, and at the age of 63 he was anxious about the journey. In his youth he had been an eager traveller, but years of the quiet life and four decades in the same job had left him intimidated by new experiences. He was fearful of making decisions, of the success of the journey depending on himself alone. My mother helped him to choose a suitable tour for them. With a guide and an itinerary he felt more at ease, and in the intervening six months he became increasingly excited about the trip.

I was living in Australia at the time, and once a week my father would send me an email telling me about his days. There was little to report, of course. By then he had settled into retirement. Moss grew on the tiled roof of the house and in between the slate patches that made up the pathway to the front door. Behind the shutters geckoes lay, blinking in the shade, waiting for nightfall when they would come out and feed on mosquitoes. Around the side of the house, beside the original front door which had already been bricked up when my parents moved in, he had glued green mesh over the air vent where wasps were trying to nest. It was only a day before my mother noticed the mess he had made; the clogged netting which he had tried to paint over in order to camouflage it from passers-by.

He woke each morning with something like a sigh and stumbled on his old knees to the bathroom's olive green basin where some days he chose to forego the slow pleasure of shaving. He retrieved the newspaper from where it lay in the driveway and read the front page with another sigh as he buttered toast for himself, complaining down the hall that the weather was different from what he'd heard on the news the evening before.

There were days that he did not leave the house. Rehearsing in the kitchen the process of making tea; sitting in his chair to do the crossword, his left hand on his brow as though in prayer. Mid-morning he would step outside onto the slate walkway and check for post, or stand on the front doorstep, looking out at his roses, glaring at the mole-damage to the lawn. Afterwards he retired to his bed and read from one of four fat books of humorous quotations he had received as gifts over several Father's Days. He read without any change of expression, before dropping the weight of the book on his chest and sleeping, his glasses still on. Later he might wake long enough to remove the book and glasses to the nightstand and curl up with the blanket around his ears like a child napping after a meal.

When my mother returned home in the late afternoon, he jumped at the opportunity of her company with a grumpy tenderness that only the old and solitary can charm. He then told her stories he had somehow picked up or created during the day, or spoke with amazement of the growth of the broccoli in the small vegetable patch that he helped her tend. By 8 o'clock he mentioned his tiredness and would rise for bed, while my mother sat up until midnight, reading or watching TV alone. An email from the time shows the emptiness of those days:

Hallo girl. Hope you had a good Saturday. First day for a week that we didn't have rain, so there were 5 bundles of washing, and then I spent over an hour scooping all the leaves out of the pool. We had over 85mm of rain this week. The little subway under the railway bridge next to Wittebome Station was awash as the Council hadn't cleaned out the muck from the drains yet (tell me the old, old story!!) and some idiot thought he could get through, but he ended up on the roof of his car. The whole car was under water. There was a picture of him sitting on the roof of his car in the *Bulletin* which I wanted to send to you, but the paper just disappeared. Anyway today was a wonderful day – no wind and clear and sunny, until about 4pm, when the cold crept in.

After the trip to Russia, the change in his emails is apparent. He wrote with an enthusiasm I did not recognise:

Hallo girl – just a short note to say we arrived back in Cape Town at about 12:00 today. The tour was unbelievably wonderful. I think it's going to take me about a week to re-adjust my thinking and slot in all we saw. The combination of history, religion, Soviet and modern eras mixing, the sights of the old, like St Petersburg compared with the new, like Moscow, and then we have to re-adjust to the old world, Tsarist Russian villages that seem to have remained the same within this great modern shift. It's almost mindboggling. All the sights and thoughts and newness and ancient, and the things we saw – Alexandra's wedding dress, and the cathedrals and the palaces (the Peterhof palace gardens which we saw yesterday are totally beyond description). And the little rundown villages and everything. It's all too much to take in. It needs a lot of thinking about. Luckily we took lots and lots of photos. Saw the embalmed Lenin, rather frightening – looked like a Madame Tussaud's wax dummy, but the dresses of Alexandra. To think that our relation (Adriana Leibbrandt) saw her in them!!

Two things stand out to me as I read this email more than two years later: the references to Adriana Leibbrandt and the embalmed Lenin.

Though we have always claimed her as our own with a sense of pride, Adriana Leibbrandt is a distant relative without any blood ties to the Jennings family. My grandmother's mother, Anna de Wet, had a sister Maria, known to most as Ria (pronounced Rye-a). Ria began a courtship with her brother-in-law, Frederick Leibbrandt, while she was working in a shoe store in Plein Street in Cape Town. He worked in a tobacconist's opposite. After marriage, they had two sons, Aubrey and Victor. In the 1930s Victor Leibbrandt volunteered to fight with the South African forces 'up north' to help drive out the Italians from Abyssinia. Afterwards he remained to fight in the war against the Germans and Italians in North Africa. Kathleen Jennings, my paternal grandfather's youngest sister, had been my grandmother's bridesmaid at her wedding in 1944. Victor, my grandmother's cousin, received photographs of the wedding while at war. In them he would have seen a Kathleen unrecognisable to those who knew her in later life. A slim, dark-haired woman, her face bright and engaging; there was no sign of the bitterness which would later characterise her. In the trenches, Victor fell in love with the image of a girl, and upon his return home he courted and married her with little pause between.

Frederick Leibbrandt was the only son of his parents, but he had four sisters. His eldest sister, Catharina, married his wife's brother. His third sister, Anna Marthina, married a Norwegian, Lauritz Andersen, who worked for a time in Johannesburg before moving to Lima, Peru. Anna's second eldest sister, Johanna (Joey), was asked to accompany them to Peru to be a companion to the family. The youngest sister, Adriana, was an accomplished concert pianist and music teacher. She eventually became one of the music teachers to the children of the last Russian Tsar, Nicholas II, in St Petersburg. There is no consensus in the family as to how this happened. Some have suggested that she was jilted after following her lover to Russia. Others argue that she was recommended to the Tsarina by the letter of a Russian nobleman who had been visiting South Africa. In any event, Adriana was with the royal family from 1910 till 1917. There is no record of how Adriana might have felt as revolution broke out around her in October 1917. No evidence of what a loss the deaths of her pupils might have been to her, nor of how near she may have come to death herself. It is only known that she was able to flee, reaching Odessa on the Black Sea, where she gained passage on a ship bound for France. There she was taken under the wing of a Polish nobleman, Count Bellinski (or Belinksi), whom she had known during her time in St Petersburg. They married, moving to a house near Regent's Park in London. Adriana remained there until her death in 1972.

Her will gives insight into how she might have lived, for she left the house to her housekeeper and its furniture to the head maid. She had no children, nor did she have any relatives nearby. All of her money and jewellery was bequeathed to her spinster sister, Joey. However, Joey (and her other siblings) had predeceased Adriana and therefore her estate was divided among the sons and daughters of her brothers and sisters. In South Africa, Victor, Aubrey and their cousin Toni each received a share of the estate. Most of the jewellery ended up with Aubrey, though he gave some items to Victor and Kathleen. Upon Kathleen's death in 2007, my sister and I inherited those few items. Amongst the opals and rubies are two large diamond rings for our respective engagements.

Frederick was a hoarder (as his son Aubrey would be too) and in one of the cellars under his house he stored all the cards and letters that his sisters had sent him from Peru, England and Russia. But, after his death, grief-stricken, Ria cleared out the cellars. On the lawn of the family home she piled letters, photos, books, portraits, everything flammable, feeding a bonfire as one might feed a hungry animal. Memories she no longer wanted access to were incinerated as she wiped soot from her eyes, her hair singed by the heat of the flames.

Despite not being with my parents on their Russian tour, I have relived that journey many times through the meticulous photo-diary that my father compiled upon his return. The notebook displays the best of the thousand or more photos that they had taken, but pride of place in the book is given to a small picture that my father printed off the internet: Lenin lying on display in the Lenin Mausoleum on Red Square, beside the Kremlin. Though the email sent on the day of his return from Russia does not suggest it, viewing Lenin's embalmed body was the highlight of the trip for my father. To see the man whom he had read so much about and whose name lined our bookshelves was an event he did not easily forget. Many times in the succeeding months and in the months of his chemotherapy, I came upon my father paging through that notebook, calling me over to recount certain memories, lingering always on the paper printout of the embalmed Lenin.

Following Siberian exile for the publication of the illegal newspaper *The Workers' Cause*, Vladimir Ilyich Ulyanov took on the pseudonym 'Lenin'. It was fashioned after the river Lena in Siberia, a name simple in its meaning of 'large river'. The man was astute, anticipating betrayals and loyalties long before they might occur. This instinct assisted him in a political career that was prolific, memorable, even inevitable. As with any individual in power, Lenin grew increasingly suspicious, frightened by his failures. His attempts at bringing socialism to the people were met with factions, civil war, a devastating famine. He saw perfidy all around him, and ineptitude. He was driven by the lot of the peasants, but they irked him too, causing him to be both penitent and angered by their lack of will to rise from their poverty and work towards a united Russia. Disappointments weakened the man, and he suffered the first of three strokes in May 1922. He was unable to speak for weeks, and movement on his right side was affected. In December of the same year a second stroke left his right side partly paralysed, causing Lenin to withdraw from active politics. In March 1923, he suffered a third stroke and was rendered mute and bed-ridden until his death almost a year later on 21 January 1924.

Over time, the cause of the man's death has been disputed. A statement made by scientist Ivan Pavlov that 'the revolution was made by a madman with syphilis of the brain' is not supported by official records. Instead arteriosclerosis (a medical issue sharing characteristics with syphilis) was the authorised diagnosis. Medical reports believed to have been adjusted and manufactured by doctors in the pay of the Soviet government make present-day diagnosis difficult, yet in 2012, at the 19th annual clinicopathology conference on deaths of famous people at the University of Maryland, two experts were called upon to solve the mystery of Lenin's death: Dr Harry Vintners, professor of neurology and neuropathology at the University of California, Los Angeles, and Dr Lev Lurie, a Russian historian from St Petersburg.

For Vintners, syphilis as cause of death was not a possibility. Autopsy revealed no evidence of the disease, nor did a syphilis test taken while the leader was still alive. In any event, Lenin was treated with a solution containing arsenic which would have, if not cured him, at least held the disease at bay. Of more interest to Vintners was Lenin's family history. His father died at the age of 54 from a cerebral haemorrhage. His brother, Alexandr, was executed at age 21 for plotting to assassinate Emperor Alexander III, and another brother died of typhoid at 19. Three of Lenin's siblings lived longer than himself. A sister died of a stroke at the age of 71, another sister died of a heart attack at 59, and a brother died at age 69 of stenocardia, an archaic medical term for angina. Lenin's family history suggests a tendency towards cardiovascular disease. A predisposition towards very high cholesterol would have ultimately resulted in Lenin's strokes. Stress would have compounded the situation. As Vintners noted, 'Stress also is a risk factor for strokes, and there's no question the communist revolutionary was under plenty of that. People were always trying to assassinate him, for example.'

In his final years, Lenin suffered the three strokes already mentioned. His death, however, was preceded by severe convulsions consistent with poisoning. Dr Lurie argues that poisoning by Stalin was the most likely immediate cause of Lenin's death. Ruthless and power-hungry, Stalin saw Lenin transfer his support from himself to his rival Trotsky. Anticipating an attack by the weakened man, he provided evidence of his fealty, sending a top-secret note to the Politburo in 1923 claiming that Lenin had asked to be put out of his misery: 'On Saturday, March 17th in the strictest secrecy Comrade Krupskaya told me of "Vladimir Ilyich's request to Stalin", namely that I, Stalin, should take the responsibility for finding and administering to Lenin a dose of potassium cyanide. I felt it impossible to refuse him, and declared: "I would like Vladimir Ilyich to be reassured and to believe that when it is necessary I will fulfil his demand without hesitation."' Yet, Stalin's sense of duty failed him: 'I do not have the strength to carry out Ilyich's request and I have to decline this mission, however humane and necessary it might be, and I therefore report this to the members of the Politburo.' But still the likelihood remains that Stalin may well have poisoned Lenin despite this assurance, benefiting by removing the leader without being seen to have blood on his hands. An order that no toxicology be done on Lenin's tissues was given after death. While heredity played a large part in Lenin's general decline, the probability is that poisoning was the immediate cause of his death.

Both Lenin and his father died aged 54. My grandfather died at the age of 63 and my father set the time of his own death by the same clock. His conviction increased after he was diagnosed with haemochromatosis.

A decade or more had seen the health of my father's aunt, Kathleen, declining. Heaviness overtook her body, her heart beat with an irregular rhythm. She tasted blood where there was none. Tests were conducted that determined she was suffering from haemochromatosis, an hereditary disease prevalent in South Africa, Canada and Australia, commonly found in people of Dutch, Huguenot and Irish descent. Unable to absorb ingested iron, the body stores the excess in various bones and organs. In the past, sufferers died from organ failure, the illness being unknown. After an examination of her family's medical history, Kathleen's doctor suggested that her mother, her sister and her two brothers (one of them being my father's father) had all died from this disease. When she was first tested her iron level was over 3,000 (normal levels should be between 150 and 250). Through regular draining of her blood it came down to 1,000 but too much damage had already been done to her heart, resulting in her death by heart failure – the same as her mother, brothers and sister.

For years, since his university days, my father's afternoons brought him to his bed, nauseous and lethargic. In 2004 a ferritin test revealed that he had an iron level of 960. With leeching he was able to get his levels down and maintain them, though by then the extra iron had been stored in his liver, hip bones and pancreas, causing him to develop type 2 diabetes. In the end, my father did not die at the same age as his father, nor from the same cause. Instead, he lived two years longer.

In the New Room – an addition to the house a decade before – my father sat in the chair that my mother's father had made, paging through the Russian photo-diary. 'He was a wax dummy, not real,' he told me again about his experience of seeing Lenin. 'It was unnerving and I felt that I didn't want to breathe in that air. It was like being in an underground cave. There was nothing real about it – the place, the man. It was something that had been created. I might as well have been paging through a picture book or seen a representation made in clay.'

'But wasn't it interesting?' I asked. 'How did he look, really?'

'He wasn't dead. He wasn't alive. He'd become something else. He wasn't there, not really. I don't know. It wasn't a person anymore. Like I said, it was something created. A body that had been put together and never been given life.'

Within a day or two of Lenin's death, a decision was made by the Politburo to embalm his body and make it available for public viewing. Pathologist Alexei Ivanovich Abrikosov was approached with the task of embalming the leader. Obscure now, Abrikosov was a great pathologist in his day, known particularly for his work in the field of tuberculosis. I knew of him in another form, under another name, for many years before researching the subject of Lenin's embalming. For months I had seen a slim volume in a book store. It had a green cover with a frog on it, and while I was drawn in by the opening pages, I was never able to justify spending a large amount of money on so slight a book, barely 100 pages in length. Eventually, however, I gave in and bought a copy. It was Mikhail Bulgakov's novella *The Fatal Eggs*, written in the year of Lenin's death and the first of Bulgakov's works to attract widespread attention before the success of *The White Guard* and *The Master and Margarita*.

The protagonist, Professor Persikov, is believed to have been based on Abrikosov (in Russian 'abrikos' means apricot and 'persik' means peach). Four years in the future, a prosperous Moscow has managed to recover admirably after the Civil War. At the Zoological Institute, Professor Persikov makes a remarkable discovery when he notices that his out-of-focus microscope produces a ray of red light. Amoebas that are exposed to this ray reproduce with rapidity and aggression. At the same time, the whole of Soviet Russia is affected by an unknown plague that attacks domesticated chickens. Not a single chicken remains. Official permission is given to a man named Rokk to use Persikov's invention to restore the chicken populace. A mix-up ensues and Rokk accidentally breeds a race of gargantuan crocodiles and snakes. These creatures escape and embark on a killing spree. The army is sent in to annihilate them. In the end, however, it is an unseasonable cold spell that kills the creatures.

Of course it is no coincidence that the ray is red. The book is, in part, an attack on the Bolshevik belief that scientific development could lead to human perfection. Written in the same year as *The Fatal Eggs*, Trotsky's *Literature and Revolution* describes an ideal world in which man will be free to alter nature to his own wishes. He will be able to change the course of rivers, to restructure mountains, and generally rearrange the planet. Yet, as *The Fatal Eggs* suggests, the new 'red' society is helpless when confronted by the forces of nature: the chicken plague comes and goes mysteriously without human intervention, and Rokk's creatures are wiped out by an unforeseen natural event, rather than the numerous high-tech weapons that are marched out against them. Surprisingly, Bulgakov's critique went relatively unpunished; he faced only several interrogations and rather than the expected exile, he was denied the option of leaving the Soviet Union.

At the age of 48, Mikhail Bulgakov died from an inherited kidney disorder. His father had died of the same disease, and Bulgakov had been anticipating his own death in the same way since his youth.

The Soviet belief in controlling nature is nowhere more prevalent than in the embalming of their great leader. For nine decades scores of people, billions of roubles and vast amounts of time and energy have been dedicated to staving off decomposition of the deceased Lenin. The process of embalming, as with any method of rendering the dead presentable, is a complex one. There are two approaches available to embalmers, depending on the length of time that preservation is required. The first is light embalming, common amongst funeral directors as a temporary solution for keeping the corpse fresh until burial. Embalming fluid, which contains formaldehyde, is injected into an artery to stay the process of decomposition.

Long-term preservation of the dead requires greater expertise and a considerable amount of effort and motivation. Major vessels and veins are opened, drained of their contents. The vascular system is flushed with a particular solution comprised of alcohol, glycerol (to prevent the body from dehydrating) and formalin (which kills off all bacteria). In order to give the body a realistic look, a pinkish tint is added to the solution. The corpse needs to be kept at a stable temperature and humidity and bathed regularly. Once every year to 18 months, the mausoleum on Red Square is closed for approximately six weeks as Lenin's remains are immersed in a bath of glycerol and potassium acetate. The skin slowly absorbs the solution, regaining its moisture and pliancy. Weekly skin examinations are performed using precision, Russian-made instruments that measure the body's moisture, colour and contour.

In 1924, Doctor Boris Zbarsky participated in the original embalming of Lenin. Ten years later his son, Ilya, followed in his footsteps, serving on the same team until he retired from his post in 1952. According to Ilya, with modern techniques the body could last 'many decades, even for 100 years'. But the threat of decomposition is always present. Mould grows on the embalmed. No matter what the precautions, bacteria will emerge, forming dark patches. Hands and faces are particularly susceptible. The first time this happened with Lenin, the scientists became terrified. A mysterious black spot of mould had appeared on his right cheek. Failure to remove the spot would result in death or banishment to a Siberian prison camp. 'The atmosphere of fear and terror was there for us scientists, just as it was for everyone in the society,' said Ilya. Fortunately he was able to remove the mould himself by means of certain disinfectants. After retirement, without any warning, Ilya and his father were arrested and accused of being German spies. Boris Zbarsky was imprisoned and his son placed under house arrest. They suffered this half-life until Stalin's death the following year. After the collapse of the Soviet Union in 1991, Ilya examined his file in the KGB archives. There he read that in 1949 he and his father had been denounced for 'counter-revolutionary conversations' – a catch-all phrase in paranoid times. In the margin of the report, in Stalin's handwriting was a note: 'Must not be touched until substitute is found.' No doubt it is for this reason that Ilya's arrest was postponed until he left his post in 1952.

The cost of preserving a body is roughly $300,000 per year. Until 1991 the preservation was government funded. But as part of a move made by the new government to step away from its socialist past, Yeltsin rescinded the payment for Lenin's upkeep. It is now funded by donations made to the Lenin's Tomb Fund. One of the surprising costs of the maintenance is that Lenin requires a newly tailored suit of clothes, including a trademark white-spotted tie, every 18 to 36 months. The custom-made suits are composed of Swiss lustrine, the fabric which Lenin preferred when he was alive. A newspaper article from 2009 reports that due to an economic crisis, Lenin's suit has not been changed since 2003. Unable to afford new suits, the specialists have been depending on steam-cleaning the old one.

The dead may have their wishes about how to be remembered. But as breath ceases, they relinquish those wishes. Mourning, reminiscence, commemoration are variously experienced by those left behind. Motivations might differ from those of the deceased. My father, according to his wishes, was cremated, to be scattered where his mother's remains had been strewn some years before. But the wooden box containing his ashes sits in my mother's cupboard, underneath two jerseys of his that she cannot part with. He will lie there some time yet,

until she is ready to give him up and place her ha
heavy with ash and bone. A new place for the
have to be found. In the botanical gardens my
ashes have been covered by a walkway; all day tourists
where she lies.

Immediately after his death, the decision was made to display Lenin's body. Due reverence for the leader of the people had to be shown. But also, a display of the leader would cement the Cult of Lenin into a secular religion across the land, managing the loyalty of the populace for those who followed him into power. For years the cult had slowly been taking shape. Portraits and busts of Lenin were the icons of worship, found side by side with icons of saints in churches and in homes, even in those of peasants. Lenin Corners (rooms or parts of rooms displaying his portraits and books) were designated as local or domestic shrines. His works and biographies were considered to be sacred writings, and these were turned to in a type of bibliomancy. Images of Lenin appeared everywhere – busts and portraits could be found in all offices, schoolrooms and factories. Posters lined the streets. His image was imposed on everyday objects like buttons and light bulbs. He was raised to a Christ-like status and worshipped across the Soviet Empire. A popular slogan from the time indicates the revolutionary's immortality: *Lenin lived. Lenin lives. Lenin will live.* Stalin's promotion of the Cult suggested that he was Lenin's representative on earth, much as the Divine Right of Kings had done centuries before.

The major state shrine for the Cult of Lenin is the mausoleum on Red Square containing his embalmed body. Despite Lenin's wishes to be buried beside his mother and despite his widow's plea, 'Do not put up buildings or monuments in his name', two days after Lenin's death, the Politburo approached architect Alexey Shchusev to build a tomb in which mourners could come to pay their respects to the great leader. Red Army soldiers had to use dynamite to blast open the winter-hard earth in Red Square for its construction. One million people visited the mausoleum in the first six weeks. Photographs taken at the time show bitter snow, yet thousands of mourners line the streets waiting to see their leader, carrying banners: 'The revolution lives on', 'Lenin is our immortality'.

By 1929, five years after Abrikosov had begun the preservation of Lenin's corpse, it was seen that the process was still working and consequently a new mausoleum was built for future generations. It was composed of marble, granite and labradorite. In the 1930s platforms of granite were added, which became the stage from which government officials inspected parades. Hidden in the depths of the mausoleum are two underground floors with a rest area for VIPs and Kremlin guards and a lab for embalming. Neither of these is used any longer and they are closed to the public. The room in which Lenin lies is the same one that appears in my father's paper print-out. It is the same one too where my father visited the embalmed man. His experience in the tomb would have been much the same as those of visitors in the 1920s. Armed guards rush tourists along in a queue that is constantly on the move. There may be no talking. No hands in pockets. No hats. No cameras. At all times a silent reverence must be kept. There may be no standing still beside the embalmed Lenin – only a cursory look, before being shunted along to make way for the endless queue of tourists and devotees.

We made no promises to one another, my father and I. Not even the promise of love or memory was spoken. His decline was too rapid, in the end, to say things either of us might have intended. Only death was a promise, and relief at his passing from pain. I missed my father's death by half an hour. I was in the cake aisle at Woolworths Food, buying pastries for comfort. My mother was with him when he died, holding his hand as his breathing stilled.

W.H. Auden's *Musee des Beaux Arts* had been a favourite of my father – ring-bound with other poems on pages photocopied from school anthologies, and given to me when I was 19. Lines of the poem come to me now; Auden speaking about suffering – 'Its human position: how it takes place/ While someone else is eating or opening a window or just walking dully along.' When my father died there were no baths of glycerol on hand to stay the process of decomposition, no pink tints to give him back the colour of life. In the hallway there stood no armed guards to prevent the orderly from chewing gum or a nurse from opening the wrong door. No one to mute the TV in a neighbouring room or the food trolley's regular squeak. On the way home traffic continued as ever, the traffic lights near the bridge as erratic as any day, allowing a haphazard flow in and out of the city. The neighbour's children played in their swimming pool, music from their sound system fed to us at full volume. In the garden weeds seemed to have grown among the roses, moles had raised their hills. Dust had fallen where we had sat hours before.

PART TWO: LESSONS FROM THE DEAD

It is only a few hours after my father's death that I begin to hide certain objects. I cannot say why I do this, only that there are things I feel I must immediately claim as mine. I am sickened at the thought of others touching, looking at, even referring to these items. My behaviour is secretive, selfish, yet I feel no shame. It isn't theft. These are things that my father promised me. I am stealing from no one.

Because of the structure of the house, I must pass the passage-length bookcase on the way to my bedroom, so it is here that I begin. I take two books. Only two, though there is an urge to take them all at once. The first is a 1960s Penguin paperback edition of E.M. Forster's *A Passage to India*. I have two copies of my own, but this one has my father's name written in the top right-hand corner of the front cover. More than that, it is the first copy of the book that I read. In the back of the book I am surprised to find notes in my own handwriting – the bones of something that later became a novel. The other book that I take is a copy of *1066 and All That*, a best-selling comedic history of Britain that came out in 1930. Instead of fairy tales, my father read to my sister and I from this book, resulting in an embarrassing slip of the tongue when I was 18 years old in Salisbury, staring at the Magna Carta in Charter House, loudly referring to it as the Magna Garter.

There are three other items that I take while my mother is in the front lounge with neighbours. I avoid them. As much as I want no one touching these items, I want nobody to touch me either.

In the passage, directly opposite the doorway of my bedroom, is a table that my father fashioned out of the base of an old Singer sewing machine. The treadle is heavy, but still moves if you push down with force. From the sewing machine table I take an ashtray which I have always thought belonged to my grandfather. It is in the shape of a boater hat, a pipe rests on its brim. It is poorly painted and desperately ugly, but it meant something to my grandfather and to my father, therefore it must mean something to me. I hide it in a jewellery box and do not look at it again until I am packing up my things, choosing what to take to the apartment. I am surprised to find words printed on the brim of the hat. I have never noticed them before.

With compliments from
SCAIFE'S HAIRDRESSING SALOON
Main Road. Wynberg.
Phone 0065 Claremont

Scaife is my grandmother's maiden name. The ashtray is not my grandfather's after all. Why did I always think it was?

The second thing that I take is mine already. My grandmother gave it to me, but I handed it to my father for safekeeping. I have to stand on the captain's chair in order to reach where he has hidden it inside a small travel bag at the very top of the cupboard in my parents' bedroom. Standing on the chair is strictly forbidden, so I have to be quick. It is an album of postcards that belonged to my grandmother's mother, Anna de Wet. My grandmother let me play with it as a young girl. Most of the cards in the album have been collected for display only – a popular hobby of the time, like collecting stamps. My favourite of the decorative postcards is a black and white photo of a young woman. A headband, shawl and rose have been embroidered onto the postcard to add colour and dimension. For some reason I tell myself that this is a photo of Anna de Wet. I know it isn't. There are real photos of her; one hangs in my parents' bedroom where she is posing with her little white dog, Ruby. It is sitting on a pillar beside her, looking directly at the camera. Anna, on the other hand, has her head tilted downwards, her expression demure. She looks nothing like the woman in the embroidered shawl.

Seventy-two of the postcards contain messages, many of them from the sedate courtship between George Scaife and

Anna (anglicised to Ann). I take these 72 and transcribe them
a year or more after my father's death. I do it in the evenings
while Juliano watches television. It is painstaking work. George
had terrible handwriting and irregular spelling. In transcrib-
ing I begin to see George and Ann as human; young people in
love. Their postcards are distant echoes of the ones I write to
Juliano when I travel. George wrote to Ann from the camp in
Port Elizabeth where he was a member of No. 3 Troop of the
Southern Rifles.

Nov 9th '14

Dear Ann
Just a line before I turn into bed, it is very uncomfortable
writing when you are laying on your stommach and the
candle wanting to blow out every minute. I am going to do
my first [illegible] tomorrow night so you will guess what
I will feeel like drilling all day and patroling the streets till
12 at night and then march back to camp. This card shows
you the Room I sleep in with about 12000 more men.
Good night dear Girl till we meet again.
George xxxxxx

The final item that I take is in the front lounge on one of
the kists that my dad made. It is a book, about the size of a
pack of cards, carved from stone. It lies open and reads:

In	To
Remembrance	Dear
South	Ann
African	From
Rebellion	George
1914-1915	

It is a rudimentary object, the engraving crudely executed.
Though I have no proof, I imagine George spending his free
hours carving this memento for Ann.

These few items are some of the first things I move to Juliano's flat. I do not like to leave them behind. I frame the postcard of the woman who isn't my grandmother and display it as though she were.

THE KIST

Juliano is at a conference in Istanbul when I move the kist into the apartment. It is too heavy for me to carry alone, so my mother helps. We place it beside the television, under the stairs that lead up to the bedroom on the mezzanine floor. On the inside of the lid is my father's handwriting in pencil:

Tool chest of Edwin Jennings
Brought to South Africa in the early 1900s.
When he sold his house in 1962, he wrote in
the lid that the chest was 91 years old.
Renovated 6–8 Jan 1996 by Keith Jennings,
Edwin's grandson.
80 year old teak used for skirting and lid
trimming.
Edwin Jennings 21 Aug 1892–16 May 1965
Keith Jennings 3 Nov 1946–
This chest is therefore 125 years old as of this date.

The chest came to my father when Aunty Kathleen moved into a retirement complex. Victor had been dead for some years and both their children had passed away many years before. Victor had used the kist as it was intended, for storing his tools. It was badly damaged and might easily have been used for firewood, but my father saw his grandfather's writing on the inside of the lid and chose to restore it instead. The chest was green before my father sanded it. Even now the inside remains green and small flecks of paint can be seen on the exterior in some of the smaller dents. Though we have other kists – kists my father made – it is this one that I want. Because of the history of it. Because of my father's handwriting on the lid.

A month later my mother and I are in Istanbul. We are spending two days here after a disappointing trip to Morocco. It was my parents who had planned this trip, but after my father's death I am invited to take his place. My mother adds Istanbul to the itinerary because she spent a day with my father there both before and after the Russian trip. The addition means that I miss Juliano's birthday. I call him from a payphone. He sounds depressed, quiet. He says he isn't sleeping. I tell him that I am not sleeping either. We are 500 metres from the Blue Mosque. The muezzin rouses us in the dark, pre-dawn, with a call to prayer that would wake the dead. I tell him about the hotel's garden where we eat breakfast. They have the stuffed body of a fox mounted on a rock. It is decomposing. Birds sit on it. I have to turn my head away when I eat. I ask him to which places he recommends we go, but he gives little information in his reply. When we say goodbye it feels as though I have been having a conversation with myself. I know he isn't upset with me. Only lonely. His family is far away.

My mother standing nearby is quiet too and on the verge of tears. Istanbul is beautiful and we are enjoying ourselves, but I worry for her. She is trying to replicate the time she spent here with my father. We spend hours looking for a café where she and he drank cold beer. When we find it she feels guilty about ordering wine instead. In the market I buy ornate ceramic coasters that are similar to the ones my father bought there two years before. When we are tired she wants us to find the bench where she sat with my father for half an hour in the sunlight, watching the people go by. Instead we sit on a bench under a tree, directly opposite some public toilets. The door of the toilet is labelled WC. A large American woman drags her friend away from it, declaring loudly, 'That's only for *wheelchairs* – see, WC.' My mother and I smile at each other. My father would have enjoyed this anecdote.

Later we eat at a restaurant near to the hotel. I have rice pudding that is so delicious that we go back the next day and have two helpings. The owner of the restaurant hands me a note – it is the recipe for the rice pudding, written in Turkish. I thank him, though I cannot read it. A lady sitting at the table beside ours offers to translate the recipe for us. She tells us that she is originally from Canada but came to Turkey a decade ago to spread God's word. She has a beard several centimetres in length that distracts me from what she is saying. When we leave, she blesses us and requests that we pray for Turkey. There has been conflict at its Syrian border.

At home again, I open the kist and place my mementoes from Istanbul and Morocco in it. Juliano hasn't yet cleared a place in the wardrobe for me and we have no other cupboards or drawers. Amongst the items I place in the chest are a photo that I took of my mother at the café we spent so much time looking for and a bookmark that is labelled 'Miniature Women Carpet'. It is meant to say 'woven'. Safe in an envelope are the Turkish and English versions of the rice pudding recipe. I write down the anecdote about the wheelchair toilets and place that inside the envelope too.

When we have more furniture I remove some of the items from the kist. They smell strange. Like wood and toil, or something long since been and gone. Now I store very little inside. Only items that do not retain scent.

This is my father's handwriting. It is taken from a red-spined exercise book. The front bears a label upon which my father wrote his name, once in black and outlined several times in red over the years with an idle hand. It is his 'Record of Howlers or Pullet Surprizes (Pulitzer Prizes)': laughable things his pupils wrote in exams or exercises.

> 4 June 1991. Std8. Use these words in sentences to explain their meanings.
>   a) surgeon   b) ventriloquist   c) quintuplets.
>
> 1) Ventriloquist is air that is given to a patient.
> 2) Quintuplets is tablets given to a patient.
> 3) Quintuplets are an endangered animal species
> 4) A ventriloquist is a doctor what works on your vents.
> 5) A ventriloquist is a doctor that works on your ventrils inside your body.
> 6) A quintuplets is someone who works on your chin.
> 7) It was so warm in the house that Dad put on the ventriloquist.
> 8) A ventriloquist builds air vents in buildings.
> 9) Quintuplets – five people playing in a music band.
> 10) A ventriloquist is a docktor who talks to you when you have a delicat problem.
> 11) Quintuplets is tablets you swallow with a cup of water.

My mother finds the book in his bedside cupboard when she is looking for items that she can give to St Luke's Hospice. There are things that those dying of cancer need – things that not everyone has on hand or can afford. Zinc ointment to rub on bedsores. Gloves for opening the fridge. Fortified drinks. Morphine and other drugs. Specially shaped pillows to keep the feet raised, or to support the back. A stool for showering. Balm for cracked heels. We pack up these items for Sister Chrys, who visited my father regularly in his final months. When she arrives we are looking at the Pullet Surprizes book and laughing. She joins us briefly, chuckling at a misquote from Macbeth: 'No man is born from a woman's worm.' A patient of hers has passed away in the night and she is on her way to visit the family. How can she do this, visit the dying every day?

The first entries in the book date from 1986, and carry on through to my father's retirement in December of 2007. He writes mostly in red or green ink – the colours of marker and moderator. He must have had the book on hand as he graded papers.

The final entry is from November 2010. It is a letter written as part of a school exercise. Not a single word in the letter is spelled correctly. It might have been written by a six-year-old for the sense it makes. This was the gift I gave to my father after I had stood in his shoes for ten days. The English teacher who had taken my father's place had had a nervous breakdown. It was two weeks before the final exams and they needed someone to come and teach parts of speech and finish exercises with her six classes. My father would not do it, having said on his retirement that he would never set foot in that school again. Yet he offered my services in his stead. I had lectured before, to 100, 200 university students at a time, but I had no experience with teaching high school pupils and had no preparation for what I encountered in those two weeks.

A poor education system in South Africa meant that many of these high school learners were barely literate. Many of them had parents who had never finished school, who worked menial jobs or were unemployed. Some of them came to class high or smelling of booze; disrupting the lesson with shouting and swearing. Few seemed to have much interest in the future. At home they had to contend with poverty, gangs. They didn't care about the grammar I had to rush them through to prepare them for their exams.

One boy who had been in the same grade for three years running remembered my father and said, 'Tell us stories like Mr Jennings told us.'

I stood in my father's classroom where he had taught for 40 years. 'No,' I said. 'We have to learn these parts of speech. No stories.'

After five minutes a fight broke out in the classroom and a boy ran away with a girl's textbook. The rest of the class chased him down the passage, out onto the field. I got no teaching done for the rest of the period.

When I went home my father said, 'You should have told them a story. I always told them about my travels through other countries. At least that way they learnt something about life outside of their own. Most of them have very small lives, you know, and no promise of them getting any bigger.'

The shops were closed in Mondsee. Tables outside the café bore tablecloths, but the lock on the door indicated that it was not open. Nearby, the butchery, florist and dental surgery had also locked their doors.

We had only stopped in the town, a 50-kilometre return detour during our time in Austria that we couldn't really afford, in order to see the cathedral. A drunken conversation over a beer-stained table in a bar in Salzburg the previous evening had had us reminiscing about our youths – we were 18 at the time – and a poster of the attractions in and around Salzburg that bore a picture of Julie Andrews in *The Sound of Music* caused us to begin singing songs from the musical with a nearby table of rowdy Australians. We had all arranged to meet again at the bus stop the following morning to visit Mondsee Cathedral where the wedding scene had been filmed for the MGM musical, the original, Nonnberg Abbey, not being impressive enough for Hollywood producers. Of course, the Australians didn't turn up, so we boarded alone, sleeping through the 50-minute bus ride.

Arriving in the town, we found the cathedral closed to the public until the afternoon. It was cold. Late September. Grey. The bus had left with none to return for a while yet. We stood outside, at a distance, listlessly taking photographs of the exterior of the cathedral. It was a disappointment, with its creamy yellow façade and windows that might have been seen on any suburban home the world over. Outside the cathedral, in what was nothing more than a tarred parking lot, were two rows of men in brown military uniforms. Nearby stood a huddle of cardiganed old women. The single photo that survived the exposed roll of film from that day is of this scene. It does not show the coffin being carried into the cathedral through the two rows of men, but it does capture the Austrian flag at half-mast above a trough of dead shrubs, five or six yellow daisies sticking out in the middle. The uniformed men seem bored, uncertain even. Several of them are looking over their shoulders towards the old women as though these might be their mothers, grandmothers. But for one thing, the photo is unremarkable: my father can be seen in the lower right-hand corner. His left hand is behind his back, a grey flat cap on his head. The stance, the build, the clothing are all my father's; yet it cannot be him. At the time my father was at home in Cape Town.

There is a certain aptness in his presence in this photo. A red-marbled album that lay gathering dust on the bottom of our passage-length bookcase for years bears photos of my father as Captain von Trapp in a school performance of the musical in 1982. By this time my father had been an English teacher at the school for 12 years. He had taught nowhere else. The programme, pale blue with a navy border, is displayed on the front page of the album.

The Sound of Music

25-28 August

V_____ High School

50c.

A newspaper clipping on the following page reports that despite 'only moderate resources, [the school] has come up with a gem... [with] wonderful choral arrangements, imaginative and effective sets, skilful performances and a high musical standard'. No mention of my father is made. The final page of the album bears a certificate topped with the school crest, taken, no doubt, from old stock as the date 197_ is crossed out. The certificate was awarded to him for his role as the Captain and is dated 21 October 1982, the day of my birth.

My father was a stern man with a bad temper. As children we regularly watched the video of his performance in *The Sound of Music*. The Rodgers and Hammerstein Captain von Trapp is depicted as a hard and emotionally distant man. He stifles his children and rules them with an iron fist. There are moments

48

of tenderness, but he is, above all else, strict. It isn't a surprise, perhaps, that as a small child I could not distinguish between my father and the man he had played on the stage. Only some years later, when I was at a friend's house, did I eventually see the MGM musical and understand that my father and the Captain were not the same man. In fact, the real Georg von Trapp was kind and warm-hearted. It was Maria who was prone to temper tantrums; yelling, throwing things and slamming doors.

In the school hall where he had played the Captain, a hall whose exterior is painted the same creamy yellow colour as Mondsee Cathedral, we held the memorial service for my father five days after his death. Though I had not thought of it for years, I remembered on that day, as I walked past pupils in their black school blazers, the funeral I had witnessed in Mondsee. After the service I went home and found the photograph, seeing in it for the first time the back of my father, watching.

Sitting in that hall that looked and smelled the same as it had done for all the years of my life, I smelled too the ghost of a man. A man still alive. A man in a polyester green suit, smelling of soap and armpits. A church-going man who touched girls, who stole, who was a bigot. A man who hated my father. He was not at the memorial service, but I felt him there nonetheless, this man who had taken my father's life and squashed it between his fingers. Established as an Afrikaans medium school, its name taken from proud Afrikaner heritage, for a long time the school boasted strong nationalist loyalty and took pride in its devotion to the Afrikaner flag. Over the years the school has evolved and is now a multicultural dual-medium school. But the green-suited principal that I remember from my childhood did not abandon his nationalistic leanings. He hated my father for the fact that he was English. He hated him for having graduated from the University of Cape Town – an institution that was heavily involved in opposition to apartheid. But mostly he hated my father for speaking out against him and not accepting his commands and decisions. With time this man prevented my father from putting on school shows, from taking the pupils on camps and tours. When my father applied for positions at other schools, this man suggested to their principals that my father was a drunkard, unreliable, incompetent. He told my father: 'I will make it hell for you and you will rot here.' By the time that man retired my father had lost all of his confidence and any will to change. I have thought about phoning him. But what would that amount to in the end? A nothing reply from an old man in a care home whose glory days have long since ended. No doubt he sits with his bitterness, as I sit with mine at a life made small.

My father had never wanted to be a teacher. In 1964, at the age of 17, he was sent to do his compulsory nine-month military service in Walvis Bay to protect South West Africa against UN forces. Photos from the time show three shirtless young men digging a trench in sand, barracks with rows of square beds. A final photograph reveals three sets of footprints in a sand dune. None of these footprints can have belonged to my father. He broke his leg during the first week of training and remained on crutches for many months. Towards the end of his service he received a letter from his father. It informed him of two things. Firstly that my grandfather had applied on his behalf for a bursary from the Cape Education Department, and secondly, that immediately after his return home he would begin working at Barclays Bank on the Foreshore. If the teaching bursary did not come through then he could pursue a career in the bank, perhaps following his father into insurance. My father had wanted to be an architect. But there was no money, and he did as he was told.

He was not a writer, my father, but some time before his death he showed me several of the poems he had written in his life. One of the more recent ones was this:

QUO VADIS?
35 years.
4 to go.
Teaching? – bloody wasted years!

In my next life
I shall be a gardener.
Plants are worth all the effort.
There are no obnoxious parents,
Rude remarks and smelly bodies.
Plants are not simpletons, grey-cell deficient clods,
Who plod through an existence of
Soap operas
Jerry Springer
Wrestling and
Fast foods.
Plants produce results –
Distinctions in shape and hue and scent.
And silence.
After 35 years
What I need is
The screaming ecstasy of silence.

We are disappointed in our parents. We find out that they are commonplace. That they have been limited by others and themselves. So we carry bitterness on their behalf, but mostly on ours, that they were not greater. That they were not Captain von Trapp or the star of an MGM musical. That they had to live a life of smallness. Was it weakness on my father's part? Staying in a job he grew to hate, allowing rumours to be spread about him. Letting his life be reduced to something so far from what he had wanted. Perhaps, though, it was something both unlike and akin to weakness. Perhaps it was love that made him stay where he was for 40 years. He kept us clothed and fed and had a ready audience five days a week to listen to his stories. In shops we would bump into his pupils, past and present. 'Is this the baby?' they would ask about me, knowing my life as intimately as though they had lived it themselves.

In an album long forgotten, in which the photos fall out as you turn the pages, there are pictures taken by my father in 1973 when he toured through Europe for the second time. Across two of the pages are spread ten photos of Mondsee and Salzburg. In Mondsee he took a photo of a vegetable market, of a street with a no-entry sign on the corner. There is no picture of the cathedral. In Salzburg there is snow; women in gloves and hats stand beside snow-covered cars. One of the photos shows him asleep on a bus. Who took this photo? The Austria of my father bears no resemblance to the one that I visited. They are separated by years and seasons.

Seeing pictures of my father posing in snow-scenes, his arms around people I do not know, I wonder at this man who in later life locked all the doors at 6pm and was in bed by 8. My father lived in Plumstead for almost his whole life, moving 11 times in his first 18 years. There was the house in Basil Road, others in Melville and Morton Roads, as well as three separate houses in Totnes Road over the years. After marriage, he chose a house in Ashbury Road and lived there until his death more than three decades later. Recently I drove through the area, visiting the houses in the order in which the family had lived in them. I criss-crossed the suburb for perhaps 20 minutes, stopping at the corner of Melville Street and Garden Street where my father recorded having his first kiss at the age of 16 with a girl called Elizabeth. There was little else to see. The properties were high-walled, their houses invisible. Only one was exposed, its garden overgrown, an unfinished fence in front of a dilapidated house. On the wall near the front door was a brown and orange mosaic of a peacock with tiles missing.

In 1950, when my father was three years old, the family moved out of Plumstead to Muizenberg, a coastal suburb in the False Bay region of Cape Town. They lived there for two years. The block of flats in which they stayed no longer exists and has been replaced by apartments aimed at low-income families, mostly African refugees. The move was a result of my father's grandmother, Anna Scaife, developing Parkinson's disease. She'd been staying with a brother and sister-in-law in Wynberg but was getting progressively worse and needed round-the-clock care. The three-bedroom apartment in Muizenberg was large enough to accommodate the family as well as Anna and her full-time nurse. My father remembered playing on the beach with his grandmother and the nurse, and buying fruit and vegetables from the government lorry that came once a month to nearby Lakeside. These are memories that he wrote down. I do not recall him ever telling us about them.

But we visited this area often as children – our father carrying us in and out of the water, walking with us along the sand as we picked up seashells with careful hands. He took us on walks along the coastal road, taking us into the museums and antique shops that lined it. He showed us patterned plates that matched those in his grandmother's home, teacups with moustaches across the lips, a tiny armchair no bigger than my fingernail which he guessed must have been the plaything of a girl long since dead. In the ballroom of Casa Natale Labia he pointed out the increasing movement of the chandeliers at the approach of a train, making us watch quietly until it had passed and the crystals had stilled again. Once he took our hands and placed them on the cold walls of Het Posthuys. 'You're touching the oldest building in South Africa,' he told us.

Close behind Het Posthuys are recently rediscovered fortifications, left over from the Battle of Muizenberg in 1795. In May of that year the VOC became unsettled when a British fleet sailed into Simon's Bay. The governor of the Cape put his False Bay batteries on alert and dispatched military reinforcements in order to block the road. The men chose a steep part of the mountainside from where they could observe both sea and road. They quickly built three walls of rock at different heights for the troops to lie behind with their muskets. Cannon and field guns were brought from the Cape, but several of the cannon were lacking their wooden decks and had to be rested on sand. It was three months before the British made their move, sending some 1,600 men marching to the blockade. Four British warships, 160 cannon between them, followed the troops along the coast from Simon's Bay. So close were the ships to shore that the Dutch could hear conversations between the men. They would have heard the order to start firing, but not understood it. Outnumbered and forced to dig their cannon out of the sand after every shot, the Dutch lost the battle. By 16 September the British had taken possession of the Cape.

Over the following years, the Muizenberg fortifications slipped into disuse. Plants grew where rocks had been manipulated into rows on the mountainside. Cannonballs rusted in the salty air. A brown bottle that had been left behind was slowly rubbed smooth by sand and wind, before being buried completely. Yet, the place was not forgotten. A British military map from 1844 shows the old Dutch defensive lines still in place. Later, during times of crisis or paranoia, a parade ground was added, and a table constructed from a flat stone. When I visited the site in 2013 these additions were still present, as was the small flight of stairs they built over weeks of waiting. They piled rocks into walls. They watched the sea. Nothing came.

After the British occupied the Cape, Wynberg became a strategic area for them, being midway between Cape Town and Simon's Bay. A military camp was positioned on Wynberg Hill. Families followed, and entrepreneurs, who brought to the area their will to survive and make something out of nothing. Their success encouraged newcomers, many of them demobbed militiamen who saw something more promising in the Cape Colony than they did back home. However, those who returned to Britain took with them what they knew of the colony. They spoke of ready money, of vast stretches of land that were calling out for masters, a cheap labour force, slaves easily bought. To those in a country growing increasingly crowded and impoverished, the Cape beckoned as much as the New World had done before it.

In Plumstead, a small town in the county of Kent, Henry Batt Senior listened to news of the colony as he drank his beer in the local pub. He was a wealthy enough farmer, but was taken up by the spirit of empire and encouraged his son, Henry Batt Junior, to go and make a name for himself. With no financial hindrance, Henry was able to sail to the Cape, and within only a few days of arrival had purchased half of a large tract of land to the east of Wynberg – a farm established by free burghers in 1692 and formerly known as Rust en Werk. Buildings from the original seventeenth-century homestead are still used as residences in what is today Castletown Road.

Henry Batt named his half of the farm Plumstead after his native town, though to many it was known as Batt's Wood due to the large number of trees on the property. Now all that remains of the wooded area is a small boggy piece of land, litter-strewn. He bred cattle predominantly, as his father had done, but took advantage of his new life to be involved in speculations and projects that allowed him to become one of the richest land-owners in the area. He was recognised everywhere, his hand ready to shake that of any man. In the street people paused to tip their hats; at the theatre and commercial hall that he had helped to build the women curtsied and men bowed. There were many among them who owed money to this man who lent without question, charging interest higher than was necessary. He kept a shop in Longmarket Street and a store at the Follies which contained 40 stock vats, 37 leaguers of sherry wine and sundry other articles that he felt required keeping. Descendants of his slaves, living in the area still, recount memories of a kind man who set up a village on his farm for workers. He treated them well, allowing them to partake in Christmas celebrations, and in his will decreed: 'All my slaves belonging to the estate to be emancipated after our deaths (Mrs Batt and me) except three old men, Azor, Isaacs and Jan who are to fulfil their engagements and then be set free.'

Henry Batt died on 21 May 1835, having been gored to death by one of his bulls as he walked his lands. Killed for its actions, the bull was buried beside Batt at the site of the attack. On this spot his wife erected a large tomb, topped by a marble urn. For many years it stood untouched, a memory of the man who had begun the village that surrounded it. But with time the urn was lost and only found by chance a century or more later in the municipal dump. It now stands in the Company Gardens in Town.

Mrs Batt left for England shortly after her husband's death. She sold a portion of the land facing the Main Road to a wagoner and horse breeder named Philip Ryklief. He and his family followed the Islamic faith and very soon other Muslim families, many of them freed slaves, moved to the area. By 1860 a stable Islamic community had been established and a mosque was built on a section of the Ryklief land. In the big house, when the wind blew in the right direction, I'd be woken before dawn by the muezzin's call to prayer, his voice ailing over the years until his replacement took over, sharp, nasal.

On Human Rights Day Juliano and I walk through Wittebome. We are looking for what remains of the tomb of Henry Batt. I am explaining the history of the name of this area, reading to him from a pamphlet that I found at Wynberg Library. From Rust en Werk it was changed to Plumstead by Henry Batt. Then, with time, this name fell into disuse as the area became absorbed by Wynberg and was later given to the neighbouring area – the Plumstead where my father had lived and grown old. In the 1950s, classified as a Coloured Group Area, this part of Wynberg was renamed Wittebome. Many of the inhabitants continued to refer to it as Wynberg as a sign of opposition to their segregation, and post-independence it is formally referred to as East Wynberg.

We are lost, despite the pamphlet's map and the fact that for 30 years I lived 50 metres from South Road, the dividing line between the two suburbs. In the streets we pass stone cottages, the homes of freed slaves and farm workers. Many are occupied by Muslim families, but in them too now live Nigerians, Congolese refugees, Malawians who stuff post-boxes with handwritten notes, advertising their skills and availability as gardeners.

A group of seven or so children approaches us. One of the boys is on rollerblades and, seeing me with the pamphlet, asks,

56

'Aunty, what are you doing?' I tell him that we are looking for Batts Road and another boy grabs the pamphlet from my hands. For a while they try to point us in the right direction, but they disagree too much about how to get there. We are more confused than before. At last the boy on rollerblades says we can follow them. They are going near to Batts Road Park, to an old age home where they will tell the old people about human rights as part of a school project. The oldest of the group, a girl of 12 or so, has silver glitter on her eyelids and hair straightened for the occasion. She keeps saying she doesn't want to do it, she's scared, but she carries her notecards with pride and won't let anyone else touch them. One of the other children asks why I am looking for Batts Road and I tell them about Henry Batt. They laugh when I tell them that he was killed by a bull who is buried beside him. The girl with the silver makeup asks if I'm from England. When I say no, that I've lived off South Road my whole life, they look disappointed and hand back the pamphlet. The last we see of them is the boy on rollerblades sitting on the pavement removing the blades and walking into the old age home barefoot.

When we reach Batts Road Park I do not tell Juliano that I remember it now and should have been able to find it. As a teenager I used to follow the neighbourhood boys here to watch them play soccer. In the far corner of the park a homeless man sits amongst his ramshackle belongings. Another, 15 metres away, lies face down in the long grass. All around are empty wine boxes and broken beer bottles. The first Plumstead was known for its crime and drunkenness. The area today is much the same, though now the problems are largely drug related. Sometimes at night gunshots can be heard. Beside the rusty set of swings we find the stone plaque that I have read about. It is all that remains of the tomb that once stood here. Graffiti covers it and I only know what it says because it is written in the pamphlet:

This plaque marks the site
of the original tomb of Henry Batt
Founder of Plumstead village

57

There isn't much else to see. Batts Road is empty but for a man in a pair of blue overalls walking towards us. I stop him and ask whether he knows where the Pandy house is. He shakes his head. 'They lived in this road in the 80s,' I tell him. He mumbles a 'no' and walks on. Before turning the corner he looks over his shoulder at us and shakes his head again, as though we are a blur in his vision. I don't know whether the Pandy family still lives in Batts Road. All I know is that their house was the site of the arrest of a group of school pupils on 15 October 1985 who became known as the Wynberg Seven.

In the mid-1980s most coloured and black schools were involved in boycotts, protesting against apartheid and its implementation of inferior schooling for non-whites. Consequently, for most pupils attending school meant going to rallies. On this day there was a demonstration taking place at Wittebome High. Afterwards some of the pupils walked home through Batts Road. They were sullen, unsurprised perhaps by the sight of police erecting barricades nearby. In the street, women returning with groceries and old men walking in the afternoon sun paused, stepping aside to follow the progress of the blockades.

Dee Dicks and Julian Stubbs were among those who went to stand with friends on the stoep of the Pandy home. When a police van drove past they did not see who threw the stones at it. It might have been anyone out of the hundred or more people who had come to watch the area being closed off. Teargas was shot without warning, sending the onlookers running for cover in all directions. Most of them were school pupils, between the ages of 13 and 17. In the Pandy house 20 of these pupils locked themselves in a single bedroom. Julian pressed his body against the door, holding the handle fast. At the windows police were shouting, 'Skiet hier binne! Skiet hier binne!' (Shoot in here! Shoot in here!) Others broke down both front and back doors, hitting at people with quirts as they entered. There was no method in their attack, nor in the arrests that they made. They had one van. It could hold ten people; once it was full those who had not been able to flee were beaten.

At Wynberg Police Station the teenagers were charged with public violence and possession of a petrol bomb. One had been found in the vicinity, hundreds of metres away from the house. There were no marks on it to suggest that it belonged to those who had been arrested. By the time of sentencing, the original ten had been reduced to seven. Three of them were too young to face imprisonment; one girl was only 14 years old. Both Dee and Julian were given three-year sentences. Dee, 12 years later at the Truth and Reconciliation Commission hearing in Athlone, recalled her time in prison:

So when we came into prison at the female section of Pollsmoor Prison... we were isolated for two weeks, kept separate from the other prisoners and then they integrated us with the other prisoners. So we had to, adjustment was difficult, but we had to mix with the other prisoners so it was common prisoners like murderers and thieves and so on. So and when we went in I was 19 at that time. So when I was in prison I was able to, it made me strong, and I was able to cope with my situation at that time and I was also fortunate to be able to complete my matric in prison and at the time the question was asked, what did it do to you at the time and I can honestly say at the time we were heroes, at that time and it, I did not feel as if it affected me at that time, but now it seems as if it is getting worse now. So I just want to go back again... All I want to do now is cry and it is, it angers me, because I am not in control of my crying and my self-esteem and confidence is very low at present and it is very difficult for me and sometimes I am still directionless and unfocused which is like the experience that I lived through in the 80's is forever in my mind and it has become quite difficult for me to cope and it is making me very angry, because at that time I could and now I cannot.

After the imprisonment of the Wynberg Seven, mass rallies in Wittebome increased. I was not aware of them. I was a toddler at the time of the arrest of the Seven, and later, as children, we were not allowed to play near South Road.

Juliano and I take a photo of the grave each, before crossing South Road into present-day Plumstead where, at the turn of the last century, Sir Richard Southey walked around his farm, Southfield, making holes in the ground with his walking stick and dropping pine seeds from his pocket. We pass the big house which my mother has moved out of just three weeks before. My father's roses are drooping. The flowers around the tree stump in the corner are dead. The stump is from one of Southey's pine trees, which nearly fell on our house during a storm in 1989. From the road I can make out the tops of the pear and plum trees in our former backyard; all that remains of Southey's orchard. No doubt the new owner will remove them. The pears are inedible, the plum tree barren. Yet I was always proud to be living on a former orchard. The original Plumstead, Kent's Plumstead, started out as a vast Roman orchard, most likely apples, though one would like to imagine plums. But by the 1880s the farmlands and ancient plantations were gone. Instead, Plumstead had been turned into a housing development for workers at the Royal Arsenal in neighbouring Woolwich. Known by most as the Woolwich Warren, the Arsenal would have stored the munitions that were used at the Battle of Muizenberg.

We walk on to Southfield Road, which is lined on either side by Southey's original pine trees. I point out number 59 where Amelia Ball of Mrs Ball's Chutney fame lived, beginning her enterprise in the outhouse at the back of the property. Next door and three houses down live ex-pupils of my father. They are everywhere, these pupils, dotting the neighbourhood and all the neighbourhoods around. He knew about their marriages, their children, following their lives as though they were characters in a book that he did not wish to close. And yet, upon his retirement he had said to us, as sternly as though making a vow, that he would never go back to 'that place'. That he wanted nothing to do with the school ever again.

My father wanted no event to mark his passing. No funeral or memorial. Nothing in the obituary column. He wanted to be cremated, scattered, and then forgotten. Those were his wishes, written down long before his death. The paper on which he had written these instructions was wrinkled when we found it months after his death, as though it had been thrown away once and then rescued, his hand flattening out the creases and re-tracing the folds before returning it to the envelope. It was too late by then to undo the service, the hundreds of people who had come to say goodbye. Pupils he had taught, colleagues from over the years. I had questioned my mother's decision to hold the memorial at the school. 'He didn't want to set foot there,' I reminded her. 'Well, he isn't setting foot, we are,' she replied. I was angered, carrying that anger with me through the service, hearing nothing, thinking only how I hated having to say goodbye to him there.

After the service, I stood at the piano watching. I had removed myself from the event. Amongst the faces there were some I recognised, but most I didn't. In the far corner of the hall, almost in the doorway, stood a tall man, balding, middle-aged. He had a tissue to his nose, a hand over one of his eyes. I had seen this man once before; in the supermarket a year or more after my father's surgery. I had been pushing the trolley, my father walking ahead, looking for items on the shopping list. All at once this man walked up to us and took my father in his arms, sobbing unashamedly, 'Mr Jennings, oh Mr Jennings, I heard you were dead. Mr Jennings.' Over and over he repeated this, his tears wetting my father's ear and collar. Who was this man who wept for my father as though he had been his own?

Beside the piano a line formed as people came to tell me what my father had meant to them. They spoke of him as a gentleman, a man who took an interest in their lives, who inspired them to be something more than their situation might have allowed. Many referred to him with the line 'Captain, my captain' or spoke of his stories. One man wrote a letter, stating:

> Your father helped with my English and always
> encouraged me to try only to do better. He went on leave
> once, to Scotland and from there sent a postcard addressed
> to me and the standard 6a's. This was the high point of
> my school career, I felt so proud reading out the postcard
> addressed to me and the standard 6a's. From that point
> on my whole life changed and I felt worth something, I
> started playing badminton and tennis and swimming, took
> up eisteddfod and debate classes as well as drama with
> his guidance. In short your father would always be on my
> mind and was my hero for years to come. Everything I
> achieved in life can be traced back to that postcard that
> seems so small back in 1975.

I looked at the faces of these strangers, read the letters and
emails that followed the service, and wondered about my
father – a man they remembered as something gigantic. Why
didn't I know this man that they spoke of? Why was the man I
knew someone that I felt sad for? Someone that seemed lonely.
A sleeping man. A small man.

My pity is meaningless, my bitterness misplaced.

PART THREE: LIVING WITH THE DEAD

When packing up the big house, my mother found a number of cardboard boxes in the garage. They were full of toys that had belonged to my sister and I. A dog on wheels, hideous ragdolls made for us with love by my Ouma, puzzles, building blocks, a pair of pink badminton racquets from when my mother tried to get us interested in sport. In the tool cupboard we found other boxes – picture books and stories from when we were learning to read. My father had kept everything. Yet, despite his care, the books and toys were ragged, musty. We gave them to a charity. There were no grandchildren yet to share them with.

I am in my early twenties when my father dreams of his grandson. In the dream, a boy, perhaps three or four years old, takes my father's hand and they walk together. It is a dream so simple that it is easily forgotten. I do not think of it again until four days after my 29th birthday. It is the day that my father is told that the chemotherapy hasn't worked, that he has two to six months to live. My mother tells me about my father's reaction to the news. He said, 'I will never see my grandchildren.' It is then that the child of my father's dream returns to me. Only now the boy has a face. The same face that stares out from a black and white framed picture that hangs in my parents' bedroom beside the one of Anna and her dog. My father is blond in the picture, three years old, and his eyes and mouth have that same tendency towards a frown that my own have.

But there is something about my father's approaching death that causes the child of his dream to take on another, stranger form in my imagination. His face is joined by the body of a ghost-child. A ghost-child he told us about whenever we asked, though he felt shamed by the tale, as he had no belief in ghosts. During his undergraduate years at the University of Cape Town, the flat of his friend was haunted by a ghost-boy. In the night he stood beside people as they slept and, upon their startled waking, asked, 'Where is my father?' A clairvoyant was brought in.

She told the boy, 'Your father isn't here anymore.' After that he was not seen again.

In the three months that my father lives, I do not mention the dream to him, nor the ghost-child, though at night I wake up often with a start, rubbing images of the boy from my eyes, my ears ringing with the whispered query, 'Where is my father?'

Above our bed is a skylight. In winter it is battered by storms; the rain and lightning unnervingly close through the glass. In Cape Town it can rain for days without ceasing. Roads flood, shacks get washed away, trees are strewn across pavements. Every year we are amazed by it, saying, 'This is worse than last year.' At the big house winter was always colder though. The ceilings were high, the rooms large. My bedroom in particular was dark and arctic; an un-thought-through tradition from England meant that it was south-facing, sunless.

When my mother moved, we packed up everything in the house and garage, leaving the garden for the last minute. In it we left pot plants and shrubs she did not want, a mouldering bird bath inherited from Aunty Kathleen and my father's rain gauge nailed to the vine which may or may not have been part of Southey's orchard. Every morning my father went with a pencil and a notebook to check on the pool and to record whatever amount of rain might have fallen during the previous day and night. It was a private pastime. No one was invited to share in it, and he did not publish his results to us over breakfast. Only sometimes, if we spoke of the weather or if visitors were present, did he casually announce that according to his records it was the driest April in a decade or a wetter July than the previous year.

My mother bumps into our former neighbour in the grocery store. The new owner has done as we had anticipated: ripped out the pear tree. The vine and plum tree are removed soon after. My mother is sickened by this, and does not react well to the news that trucks have dropped building supplies at the house; walls are coming down and being replaced elsewhere. The old lines are being moved. 'But what can we do?' I ask her. 'It doesn't belong to us anymore.'

Weeks later I am at the municipal dump. I am dropping off our recycling and keeping an eye out for bricks which my mother has been collecting for paving the alleyway behind her house when spring arrives. It has been raining for five days straight, the noise keeping Juliano and I awake at night. I have taken to napping in the afternoons when the traffic and other sounds can lull me to sleep. As I park, the wind rips through the piles of recycling and scatters the yellow-clad men who are sorting glass from plastic. They run across the parking area, chasing ice-cream containers, empty soda bottles, a crate that should be too heavy to be moved by wind alone. To the right of me, a rain gauge, the same make and colour as my father's, rolls under the car and out the other side. It comes to rest in a puddle, gulping in water. A man in a rain-suit picks it up with gloved hands and tosses it back amongst the recycling.

I go home and try to take a nap. My head is aching, the pounding of the rain on the skylight beats through me. I can't sleep. It is raining too hard.

When I pick Juliano up at the airport he is wearing my father's grey tracksuit pants and a T-shirt wrinkled by ten hours on an aeroplane. I have already been back from Brazil for two weeks. At the time that we booked our flights we decided that he would stay longer in order to have time alone with his family and friends. I am glad that we made that decision. The three weeks with me must have been exhausting. But for his sister, the family does not speak English. I needed him constantly as a translator. The 30 or so words and phrases that I had rehearsed proudly in the weeks prior to our departure were used up within an hour of our arrival and were almost wholly useless. How could I have imagined it necessary to learn the question 'Where do you live?'

At first I was overwhelmed by his family. There are many of them and they are loud. They visit, gossip and are involved in one another's lives. They are one another's best friends, cousins are like siblings. This is not what I am used to. I have four cousins, two of whom I haven't spoken to in years and doubt I will have contact with unless a funeral demands it. My sister and I aren't close. There are no second cousins and aunties and uncles and distant relatives that we can boast having any sort of relationship with.

I could not understand what Juliano's family were saying, not beyond one word in every hundred. Instead I spent the time watching their expressions and gestures.

A big party was held in my honour so that all of Juliano's friends could meet me. There were many of them, their names rolling into one long vowel that I could not pronounce. Nervous, I drank too much *cachaça*, tried to be too impressive. As we stood around eating the *feijoada* that his mother had prepared, I tried to imitate the gestures I had been learning over the past two weeks. My hand knocked the fork on my plate, sending food catapulting over the face and body of the man beside me.

He laughed genially, as did everyone else. But I was devastated. There could be nothing worse than this embarrassment. I hid in the guest bedroom for half an hour, sipping *cachaça* to numb the humiliation.

When Juliano came to find me I noticed for the first time that he was wearing my father's tracksuit pants.

'It's a party,' I said, 'How can you be wearing those?'

'They're comfortable,' he replied.

'But you look like a homeless man. People will think I don't take care of you,' I complained. And then I laughed. How strange the way that moments echo one another, how we find ourselves reliving the same situation in new surroundings, with new people.

The history of these tracksuit pants is one of embarrassment. My father had been cold from the chemotherapy and my mother wanted him to buy a pair of pants that he could wear in public. He already owned tracksuit pants, but their knees were saggy, their material knobbly. In a hypermarket where my mother had gone to look at cameras, my father found this pair of tracksuit pants in the clothing section. I was with him as he said, 'These will do.' And I watched as he walked hurriedly to the till to pay for them before my mother could see them. She was furious when she found out. I remember taking her aside, saying, 'Let him buy the pants. He feels like you do everything for him. He feels like he isn't a man anymore.'

She turned on me, 'Don't tell me how he feels. He's my husband.' Then her face softened and she started to cry, 'He will look like an old man. People will think I don't take care of him. They will think I don't care that he is dying.'

At the airport Juliano has a mop of hair that should have been cut a month ago. The pants are stretched out and sagging. His T-shirt has a stain on it. I hug and kiss him. 'What will people say?' I ask him. 'They will wonder why I am picking up a homeless man from the airport.'

I had not met my father's sister above twice in the 24 years since she, her husband and their twin sons had emigrated to Australia. By the time that I went to stay with them in 2010, the boys were grown up and Jean and Derek had moved to Hobart, Tasmania, as a result of Jean's lupus. An autoimmune disease, lupus results in the body's immune system becoming hyperactive. It attacks normal, healthy tissue, causing inflammation, swelling, and damage to joints and organs. For Jean, the heat of the Central Coast exacerbated her symptoms, and so they chose to move to Tasmania with its cooler climate.

On the island they found a mountain-shaded suburb beside the sea, buying a large wooden home that had been built by a sea captain. The wooden floorboards, doors and window frames used in its construction were taken from abandoned ships and buildings in the Antarctic. On my arrival they spoke of the captain's presence in the house, of objects and doors moving by his hand. It was an unusual story to be told on my first night, made more so by the fact that a few days prior to my departure I had seen my first ghost: the old lady who wanders up and down the passage of the big house. There is nothing threatening or frightening in this woman. She is simply an old lady who walks the same route decade after decade. I looked up from the couch and saw her in the passageway. She was grey, peaceful. I looked away and thought nothing of it until sometime afterwards, so much did she seem a part of the house. Both my parents had witnessed her when they first bought the house, and my sister, as a young child, often said to my mom, 'There's the old lady.' Some years ago, the mother of one of my mother's pupils said that her grandparents had lived in that house and that her grandmother had died there. Perhaps that is who the old lady is. I did not see the sea captain in the Tasmania house. Nor did I hear him, though I looked for him daily.

Perhaps it is more common than we care to acknowledge,

the desire to touch the past. We do so in various ways. The memories we store, objects we display, how we engage, or attempt to, with the dead. In these ways we invite them into our houses, feeling comforted that death need not mean an end.

It was Jean who told me that neither the big house nor their Tasmanian home was the first in the family to be associated with visitations. My grandmother's cousin, Beryl, had an interest in clairvoyance. From her home in Wynberg she routinely held séances and read tarot cards or tea leaves for friends. She had many like-minded acquaintances and through them was introduced to a gentleman who called himself Tim Phat. On visiting her home he confided that there were powerful streams of cosmic energy running through it. With assistance, he believed that he could channel this energy and produce a portal to the other side. When Louis, Beryl's husband, heard the news he booked himself a three-month trip to Europe in order to avoid the visitation. Once Louis had left, Tim Phat further informed Beryl that a monetary offering to the spirits was necessary to advance 2 Remington Road to the ninth and most heavenly plain. She could then be in constant communication with anyone who had passed on. At the mention of money, investigations were done by Beryl's friends and Tim Phat was found to be a charlatan. When Louis returned from Europe, Mr Phat and the cosmic energy had disappeared and Beryl was breeding rabbits in the backyard to sell to a butcher in Ottery Road.

I moved to Tasmania temporarily, having been awarded a generous three-year scholarship by the University of Tasmania to complete a PhD. Though I had sought the scholarship, I went with a heavy heart, seeing it as nothing more than a three-year prison sentence. My father had recently recovered from the surgery to remove the cancer in his colon and though we'd been told he was well, I feared that the cancer would return while I was away. I had only applied for the scholarship as my boyfriend at the time was applying to study overseas and I didn't want to be the one that was left behind.

Though I had the fortune of staying with family, distance had rendered them little more than acquaintances. My father and Jean were born eight years apart so that he was already grown up long before he had any interest in being associated with her. Nor did she have much interest in him. He was a weak boy who spent most of his childhood ill in bed, covered in garlic and horse-dung compresses administered by his grandmother. He could not run or kick or play outside. He had no friends. His father found it difficult to relate to this sickly child and attempted to remedy the situation by dragging him to watch soccer matches every Saturday. There, in the stands, my father perfected the art of playing on his own. In the months before his death he recorded his favourite childhood pastime as being alone, occupying himself with his toys. He had been the first grandchild to survive and as a result received many gifts. These he did not play with in the conventional way. Instead he displayed the cars, train sets and farm animals on a table in his room. He laid them out in rows, according to colour, size and shape. They were not moved from these positions. Later he followed the same practice in the passage-length bookcase in the big house and we butted heads when I chose to organise my own collection of books alphabetically. Perhaps it is for these reasons that he appeared to cultivate solitude in later life and why I have inherited that trait, preferring to be alone than to be in company.

I arrived in Tasmania as a prisoner serving my time. I lived in a cell of my own making, sullen, self-pitying, exiled. It cannot have been easy for Jean and Derek, who are garrulous, generous with their time, hospitable. Yet, as the months passed, what had begun as self-pity deepened into a melancholy that rendered me suicidal. I woke each day, breathing in a black fog that would not lift. I could taste death in my mouth. I began to prepare for my passing, going about it as calmly and with as much organisation as is required for scheduling a holiday.

It was not the first time that I had planned my death. At the age of 19, halfway through my first year of university, I was admitted to a clinic. Then I had been agitated, my mental state too much on display. By now I was experienced. An ability to reason carefully had warned me that to succeed in dying I had to appear well. This I did as far as was possible. I worked on my dissertation. I ran in the evenings, wrote letters home, played with the neighbour's dog. I even swam in the icy waters of the pebbled beach near their house. Every day was a performance that I enacted. During my months in the clinic I had shared a room with a girl who was caught by one of the nurses hanging herself in the shower. She used a scarf that she had found in my cupboard. Though she survived the ordeal without harm, she told me, 'I am already dead. They just don't know it.' It was into this sort of half-life that I had convinced myself in Tasmania. As my mental state weakened, I believed myself to be someone already dead. I was a ghost. At night I no longer slept. Instead I waited for the sea captain to appear. In seeing him, I believed my death would be confirmed.

I told no one of my plan to die, of my paranoia and strange imaginings. Yet there must have been something in my expression that suggested my unhappiness. At the height of my depression, Jean and Derek surprised me by taking me away for the weekend. We were to go to Port Arthur, a nineteenth-century penal colony that was my father's favourite site during the single visit he ever made to his sister several years previously.

One approaches Port Arthur via the Tasman Highway before turning onto the Arthur Highway that leads towards the ruins of the settlement. The island is small and a drive of this distance takes longer than necessary only because of the many stops along the way to view the scenery. Cliffs and a blue ocean can be seen at certain points. Greenery is everywhere. Trees as old as the world itself line the way. And, every ten or so metres there is the sight of a dead possum, wombat or wallaby. They mark the roads of the island, which is known as the roadkill capital of the world. On average 32 animals are killed per hour, approaching half a million per year. The locals boast that it is because they have so much wildlife that there is such a large amount of roadkill. Yet there is more than one species that is endangered.

We pass a family of wallabies. Three of them, all dead in a row. A wombat on its side, its mouth open, as though preparing to bite the ground. A possum that crows have visited. There is little blood associated with roadkill. Perhaps only, should you take the time to look closely enough, can you see blood at the mouth. Otherwise, injuries tend to be internal. The animals lie on the side of the road and, if not dead on impact, can stay there for many days before dying. Some are rescued, others recycled.

We pass a man with a trash bag picking up the bodies of the dead. He has on thick gloves, but his legs are bare below his shorts. Jean tells me he is from the Tasmanian Devil sanctuary that we will pass shortly. Devils are scavengers and feed on the dead in the wild. It is one of the reasons for their endangered status. Many of them are hit by cars when eating the bodies on the road. But mostly, they are being wiped out by Devil Facial Tumour Disease – a transmissible parasitic cancer that forms lesions in and around the mouth. It is spread when they fight. Tumours grow on their faces where bites have occurred and interfere with eating; they starve to death. In less than 20 years the population has dwindled by 70 per cent. The threat of their extinction is very near, yet their bodies are amongst those that we see beside the road as we drive.

The eighteenth century saw the growth of large-scale capitalist agriculture and industry in Britain. With it came poverty, social injustice, child labour and long working hours. The population, which had remained a steady six million from 1700 to 1740, rose dramatically. London became overcrowded, flooded with cheap gin and crime. Prisons were full, no person was safe from the law. This was due largely to the Bloody Code – a system of laws and punishments that by the 1770s boasted 222 crimes that carried the death penalty, including cutting down a tree, sending a threatening letter and stealing from a rabbit warren.

By 1800 the death sentence was considered too harsh a punishment for many of these crimes. Instead, transportation became the more common penalty. Records show the letters *YT & PS* beside criminals' names; shorthand that meant 'Years transportation and penal servitude'. There seems to have been no consistency in the meting out of punishments. Records from Gloucester Assizes on 3 August 1825 show that William Williams was imprisoned for three years for the attempted rape of ten-year-old Hannah Roberts, James Turner received the death sentence for theft of a hat, while William Chivers was sentenced to transportation for life for stealing 21 cheeses from Francis Cam. Most transportation sentences were for the periods of seven or fourteen years; however, no assistance was given for their return after their time had been served. It was up to them to go back under their own steam, the hope being that they would not be able to, and England would be rid of generations of criminals.

However, by 1833 the colony was facing difficulties with some of its transported criminals. It was not enough for them to have been exiled to Australia; it did not appear to have cured their evil natures. Whipping and other punishments did not prevent them from stealing, brawling or attempting to escape. As a result, secondary offenders were sent to Port Arthur on the rugged Tasman Peninsula for further penance. The Tasman Peninsula is separated from the island by a thin strip of land known as Eaglehawk Neck. Other than the 30 metres that comprise the Neck, the sea is the only possible means of escape. In the nineteenth century it was not common to find people able to swim, not even amongst sailors. Should a man have contemplated the idea of escape by means of swimming, the guards let it be known that the seas around the peninsula were full of sharks. Mantraps were used along the strip of land, as well as a military guard which included a line of dogs. These were chained close together, some on pontoons built in water alongside the Neck. Bronze statues commemorate these dogs on either side of the road as one crosses Eaglehawk Neck. Jean takes a photo of me beside one of these statues, my hand in its mouth, my face contorted in a show of agony.

At the time the island of Tasmania was known as Van Diemen's Land, named after Anthony van Diemen, the Governor-General of the Dutch East Indies, though for the British the word had associations with demons. By title alone it promised that its new inhabitants would find their pasts haunting them blackly. The island became a source of fear amongst the British and their prisoners, and soon the place was as much ingrained in their mythology as King Arthur and his knights. Men recorded their fear of the place in a ballad, and the hulks in the river Thames that housed those waiting for transportation swayed with the sound of it.

> Come, all you gallant poachers,
> That ramble free from care,
> That walk out of a moonlight night,
> With your dog, your gun, and snare;
> Where the lusty hare and pheasant
> You have at your command,
> Not thinking that your last career
> Is on Van Diemen's Land
>
> Oh! when that we were landed
> Upon that fatal shore,
> The planters they came flocking round,
> Full twenty score or more;
> They ranked us up like horses,
> And sold us out of hand,
> They yoked us to the plough, my boys,
> To plough Van Diemen's Land.
>
> God bless our wives and families,
> Likewise that happy shore,
> That isle of sweet contentment
> Which we shall see no more.

As for our wretched females,
See them we seldom can,
There are twenty to one woman
Upon Van Diemen's Land.

Come all you gallant poachers,
Give ear unto my song,
It is a bit of good advice,
Although it is not long:
Lay by your dog and snare;
To you I do speak plain,
If you knew the hardships we endure
You ne'er would poach again.

Besides the rough journey and labour, the song speaks of loss, of being exiled from loved ones. It is a song of isolation.

They were not wrong, those who sang of isolation. Imprisonment at Port Arthur was founded on the concepts of separation and seclusion. Punishment was psychological rather than physical, influenced by the thinking of British social reformer and philosopher Jeremy Bentham. He called for the abolition of physical punishment, as whipping, he argued, only hardened criminals. Instead food became a means of rewarding the well behaved. They benefited from allowances of tea, sugar, tobacco. The badly behaved were given only bread and water. Bentham also designed the panopticon – a type of circular building that allowed a watchman to observe all inmates without their knowing whether they were being observed or not. One of the benefits, he argued, was that fewer staff were required. One guard would suffice.

Port Arthur followed Bentham's suggestions in most particulars, except their Separate Prison was built in the shape of a cross, each wing connected to the surveillance core of the prison. Every wing could be seen, but not the individual cells. All convicts who came to Port Arthur had to spend time in the Separate Prison in order to give them the isolation required to better themselves through thought and deprivation. Twelve months' solitary confinement was regularly enforced before the prisoner was allowed to join others in the penitentiary. Silence was compulsory at all times. Thick walls and doors ensured separation and quietness. Warders patrolled in felt slippers and communicated in sign language so that the prisoners heard no sound. Men spent 23 hours a day in their cells and were allowed one hour, hooded, alone in the courtyard. Once a week, again hooded, they were led into the chapel with its specially designed private, walled-off pews. It is not surprising that many developed mental illnesses from lack of light and sound. Insanity became so regular a disorder amongst the inmates that an asylum had to be built beside the Separate Prison.

I stay a long time in the Separate Prison. Jean and Derek have wandered off and I remain, practising the silence of the inmates. The day is quiet. There are not many visitors, and for some time I am the only person in the building. I can hear no sounds entering from outdoors. There is nothing to indicate that I am not the sole inhabitant of this building, the peninsula and island, even of the world itself. I read of Leonard Hand, an Australian-born boy of 15 who was sentenced to 15 years for attempted sodomy. The photo that survives shows a handsome man, blond, clean-faced. Given the chance he might have broken many hearts. In the Separate Prison he filled his hours by making shoes seven days a week. Initially, he had attempted to communicate with other prisoners, tearing up a Bible for that purpose, but the punishment when caught was severe: 30 days in the 'dark cell' without light or exercise. Three years of solitary confinement had left the boy 'mentally childish and silly', according to Dr Covedale, Port Arthur's surgeon, who hoped to have him removed and saved. But by this time Hand was beyond saving. He sought isolation, growing panicked at the company of others, and requested to be allowed to remain in the Separate Prison. At the age of 24 he was removed to Hobart Gaol and died soon afterwards. The medical report states the cause of his death as 'natural', though in all likelihood he was unable to reconcile himself to sunlight and the company of others.

In all that silence and loneliness, I feel at ease. It does not seem frightening or punishing to me. As I look at the displays, one man reminds me of my grandmother's cousin, Aubrey. The man in the photograph does not have the look of a criminal about him. Instead he is small, balding, wears glasses. A caricature of sorts, as Aubrey too had been. Aubrey was a slow-thinking, reserved person who isolated himself from the world, spending many hours in thought. Even as a child I remember feeling that he was trying too hard in company. His jokes were rehearsed, the gifts of chocolate were stale, his smile unsteady.

Sometime in the 1950s Aubrey invented and patented the little lever that one finds on shoe polish tins. This small invention made him a rich man. He was able to buy a large double-storey house in Clovelly, which despite being 500 metres from the beach, was west-facing. At no point in the house did a window look out at the sea view. In some there were no windows at all. To further secure his privacy, Aubrey bought the six empty plots around his house and let nature take its course. Trees grew, hiding the windows, bushes covered the path and spread across the lawn. The house was invisible on all sides, separating Aubrey from the rest of the neighbourhood.

In the roof of the house was a vast attic, divided into three sections. Here he stored his things, for, like his father, Frederick, he threw away nothing. Papers, photos, containers of old film, suitcases filled with clothes that he had worn, old magazines, newspapers, even a washing line heavy with dusty laundry, and hundreds of boxes filled with everything he had ever owned. All the detritus of a life lived in isolation. He was someone we always joked about, a warning – 'you're turning into Uncle Aubrey' – if any one of us spent too much time alone, stored too many tokens. Here, the echo of his face before me, I feel a kinship with this lonely relative and his strange ways.

Port Arthur was closed in 1877. By that stage the handful of men who were living there were old and feeble. They were unable to care for themselves and suffered from varying degrees of insanity. Freedom was not an option for them, and so they were sent to live out their days at the New Norfolk Insane Asylum. I have seen this building, strange and shadowy, beside the Derwent Highway, the road built by ex-convict Denis McCarty and which he is said to haunt.

Desperate men, sent mad by isolation, attempted to escape from Port Arthur. A number drowned when fleeing in canoes manufactured from the hollowed-out logs that they worked with in the timber yards. More creative attempts include that of George Hunt, who disguised himself in the hide of a kangaroo. He had been given a 14-year sentence for the theft of a handkerchief and could not face the years of labour and exile. As he approached the line of dogs at Eaglehawk Neck, mimicking the bounding of a kangaroo, the hungry guards began shooting at him. Their rations were limited and they saw little meat beyond what they could come by themselves. A kangaroo would have made a happy meal for them. At the shots, Hunt threw off his disguise and surrendered, receiving 150 lashes for his escape attempt. Others resorted to more final measurements. Pacts were made amongst pairs. One would murder the other, receiving the death sentence for his crime. Both men would be dead, and both would be free from their prison.

Yet even the dead were not wholly free from Port Arthur. Their bodies were taken to the Isle of the Dead, there to decompose and become one with the soil of the place. The selection and naming of the island as a burial ground is described in a religious pamphlet entitled 'The Isle of the Dead: Or the Burial Place at Port Arthur', which was written in 1845 by Reverend John Allen Manton, the officiating clergyman of the penal colony.

> It fell to my lot to be the first Minister of the Gospel
> appointed to preach the word of life to these degraded
> outcasts... Disease and death soon made their inroads

among us; so it was necessary some suitable spot should be selected where to deposit the earthly remains of the departed. In this spacious bay, on the verge of which the settlement is situated, at the distance of a mile, stands a lovely little island, about half a mile in circumference at the water's edge. This, it appeared to me, would be a secure and undisturbed resting-place, where the departed prisoners might be together until the morning of the resurrection.

Manton laid out a plan for the isle, insisting that social distinctions be upheld – the free were buried on the raised north-west side of the island, convicts on the lower side. Convict graves were unmarked, with nothing more than the mound of earth to indicate their position, and these rain and wind flattened with time. Furthermore, only two small structures were allowed on the isle. The first was a shelter for mourners, the second a small wooden hut that housed the gravedigger, a man who might be entirely forgotten were it not for the record made of him by British novelist Anthony Trollope when touring Australia and New Zealand in the early 1870s:

But of all the men the most singular in his fate was an Irishman, one Barron, who lived in a little island all alone; and of all the modes of life into which such a man might fall, surely his was the most wonderful. To the extent of the island he was no prisoner at all, but might wander whither he liked, might go to bed when he pleased, and get up when he pleased, might bathe and catch fish, or cultivate his little flower-garden, – and was in very truth monarch of all he surveyed. Twice a week his rations were brought to him, and in his disposal of them no one interfered with him. But he surveyed nothing but graves. All who died at Port Arthur, whether convicts or free, are buried there, and he has the task of burying them. He digs his graves, not fitfully and by hurried task-work, but

82

with thoughtful precision, – having one always made for a Roman Catholic, and one for a Protestant inmate.

He smiled when Ave asked whether the graves awed him, – but he shook his head when it was suggested to him that he might grow a few cabbages for his own use. He could eat nothing that grew from such soil. The flowers were very well, but a garden among graves was no garden for vegetables. I asked him whether he was happy. No, he was not happy. He wanted to get away and work his passage to America, and begin life afresh, though he was sixty years old. He preferred digging graves and solitude in the island, to the ordinary life of Port Arthur; he desired to remain in the island as long as he was a convict; but he was of opinion that ten years of such work ought to have earned him his freedom. 'You have no troubles here,' I said. 'I have great troubles,' he replied, 'when I walk about, thinking of my sins.' There was no hypocrisy about him, nor did he in any way cringe to us. On the contrary, he was quiet, unobtrusive, and moody. There he is still, living among the graves, – still dreaming of some future career in life, when, at last, they who have power over him shall let him go.

Upon Barron's death, after 20 years served as gravedigger on the Isle, he was replaced by 'Big Mark' Jeffrey. This man found comfort in digging his own grave and tending it carefully. All day he busied himself with patting down the sides, removing worms and fallen leaves. There he lived quietly, until one morning, mid-week, the guards spotted a signal fire coming from the Isle. When they reached him, Big Mark was in great distress and begged to be removed. He related how in the night his hut had been shaken by an invisible force and a fiery red glow lit up his surroundings. From a stinking yellow mist arose, horned and fiery, 'His Satanic Majesty' himself. It is not recorded what the devil told Big Mark, but the experience was enough to terrify him and he refused to return to the Isle. His grave caved in and filled up with leaves. Later it was used for the burial of another body, and Big Mark was sent to the Launceston Invalid Depot where he died in 1903. He was 78 years old and had spent his entire adult life in the convict system.

I find Jean and Derek in the Memorial Garden. We are all tired and hungry and want to have a rest before we return in the evening for a guided ghost tour, but we take the time to sit in the garden first. It is a place of quiet reflection, designed as a memorial to the 35 people killed and 23 wounded when a young man went on a killing spree at Port Arthur on Sunday 28 April 1996. There was no motive behind these murders other than that he wished for fame by setting the record for the most people killed by a single gunman at one time. For this reason, the people of Tasmania do not say the man's name and it is rarely published. After his capture he was given 35 life sentences without the possibility of parole. A few weeks before we visit Port Arthur, I join a dinner party with Jean and Derek. There I am seated beside a doctor who attends to the prisoners at Risdon Prison. The young man is amongst his patients. The doctor tells me that the prisoner does not leave his cell, has given up speaking. His only comfort comes from regularly summoning the doctor to check his genitals, which he believes to be rotting.

It is not surprising, perhaps, given its long history of bloodshed and despair, that Port Arthur is recorded as being Australia's most haunted site. Ten thousand sightings have been reported in the past 20 years, though paranormal encounters date back to the nineteenth century. I experience nothing uncanny while on the ghost tour, not until we reach the parsonage, which is said to be the most haunted place at Port Arthur. The guide informs us that the Reverend George Eastman died in an upstairs bedroom. His body was placed in a coffin, but the bearers found it too awkward to carry down the narrow staircase of the cottage. Using a rope, they began to lower the coffin out of a window, but the rope snapped, and the coffin shattered as it hit the paving below. Reverend Eastman's corpse rolled into the gutter. To this day people report the smell of decaying flesh and strange moans coming from that place. I smell no flesh, see no lights. But the story of the coffin causes goose bumps to break out across my body, and once again I am reminded of Beryl.

My grandmother's father, George Scaife, persuaded two of his brothers to come to South Africa in order to avoid having to fight in the First World War. One of them, James, opened Scaife's barber shop on the Main Road in Wynberg. He married an Afrikaans girl, Esther van Dyk, and they lived in Broad Road in Wynberg. They had three children, Beryl, James (Jimmie) and Lesley. Jimmie became an alcoholic at a young age. His wife left him and he lost his job, his house, everything. Homeless, he began begging on street corners between Wynberg and Claremont, and sleeping in Maynardville Park opposite Beryl's house. By then his mind had become so addled from drinking methylated spirits that he did not know who she was. Eventually he ended up in Valkenberg Mental Institute, where he died years later.

A large, jolly lady, Beryl spent her days cooking and laughing. She fell in love and married a Jewish man, Louis Hoberman, whose family had arrived in South Africa in the 1800s. The Hobermans had gone through the usual practice of first being *smouse* (travelling salesmen) and then owning a small store, which eventually expanded into a bigger store. Louis sold ladies' underwear door-to-door in the Wellington Avenue and Wittebome areas. He kept this business going until the 1960s, by which time most of his customers had died and their daughters were not interested in buying underwear from a *smous*.

Louis was rude, moody, insular. He ignored his wife and his two children, spent Jewish holidays with his family in Sea Point and made a habit of keeping his life as separate from Beryl's as was possible when living in the same house. He gave Beryl a minimal monthly allowance for groceries which she supplemented by keeping chickens and a vegetable garden at the back of the house. He did not eat her food. Instead, he bought himself steak or smoked salmon which he prepared and ate when Beryl was not in the kitchen.

I remember Louis only with a child's mind. He has a face, but no features. We visited Beryl with my grandmother once or twice, my sister and I, walking up to Wynberg with her, standing at the garden gate, but never going inside. I don't know whether we weren't allowed in or whether my grandmother refused to enter his house. I remember her only saying 'He's a terrible man' when I pointed at his face staring at us through a window.

For my father it was different. As a child he went to Beryl's house many times, mostly on Wednesday mornings. On one of those Wednesdays they arrived to find a very old man sitting in the sun on the front porch. He was as thin as a skeleton, grey-skinned, and was wrapped in coats and blankets. Beryl explained that Louis had been contacted by the International Red Cross and told that a Lithuanian Jew who had survived the Nazi concentration camps had been found in a Polish hospital. He was the cousin of Louis's father and they were his only living relatives. The man was sent to South Africa by sea, barely surviving the voyage. Beryl cared for him, feeding him watery porridge, soup and weak tea. He spent his days sleeping or sitting in the sun. He could not speak a word of English. One morning, several months after his arrival, Beryl discovered him dead in his bed. Two days after he had died, Louis got a Rabbi to exorcise all the spirits from the old man's room. He had a paranoid fear of being haunted.

When Beryl died in 1992, in order to save money, Louis bought a traditional Jewish coffin – cheap box wood and rope handles – for Beryl's Anglican funeral. At the graveside he began wailing, falling into my father and grandmother's arms, lamenting the death of his beloved wife. All throughout the reverend's sermon Louis moaned, tugged at his hair, called out to God. Afterwards, as the coffin was lowered, it became clear that it would not fit into the grave. It was too long. What nobody had realised was that Jewish coffins have different dimensions to others. The undertakers tilted it slightly, but one end became wedged in the soil piled at the head of the grave and, being made of box wood and nailed down with tacks, the lid started to lift to reveal Beryl's pale corpse lying inside. Her eyes were open, her lips slightly parted. Louis began screaming so loudly that he had to be dragged away.

Years later when I asked my grandmother about the funeral, she told me that Louis's screams were not out of outrage or anger. He was screaming out of fear. He had seen Beryl's eye looking at him as the coffin tilted and split. He had known that he would be haunted.

When we leave Port Arthur the following day, the sickness of my depression has become so heightened that I wonder whether Jean and Derek can see me, whether they know that I am little more than a spectre in the back seat. I am ghost-ridden, mad. My brain shakes inside my skull and I fall into half-dreams where coffins open in front of me, corpses bearing the faces of my family falling from them. We stop at the Tasman Blowhole. Jean and Derek buy strawberries and cream from a café in the parking lot while I stand watching the Blowhole fill with the tide until it is no hole anymore, just water. When we get back in the car I tell them, 'I am sick. I have to go home.'

It is a few weeks before I am able to get a flight back. The Soccer World Cup is on in South Africa and planes are full.

Returning does not cure the depression, but I begin to feel less agitated, my paranoia lifts. I tell myself that it is the beginning of a new life. 'A new life' I write everywhere, as though by its writing it will be made real. Most days in the weeks after my return, I sit with my father in the new room. We watch British comedies and page through his Russia album. At night I look through the collection of poems he compiled for me almost a decade before when I was released from the clinic. It is inscribed: *To Karen who went away for a while, but who has come back.*

Six months later my father's cancer returns.

PART FOUR: CREATING THE DEAD

The Visa

I return from Brazil with little more than R200 to my name. In four weeks' time I am travelling to Arnhem in the Netherlands where I will stay for a month-long sponsored residency. For two of the four weeks I am alone; Juliano is still in Brazil. I cannot afford to buy groceries, yet I eat compulsively, everything I can find in our cupboards and whatever I can take from my mother's place when she isn't looking. I am ashamed of my poverty. It was my choice to take the year to write and so I do not mention to anyone that I misread the residency contract and that I have to pay for the visa myself. Instead I go through my bookcases ruthlessly, picking out books that I can sell. At the second-hand bookshop I am given just enough money to cover the cost of the visa. I walk away feeling like a criminal. Is this the life that I have chosen for myself?

When the visa is ready for collection, I decide to take a minibus taxi to Town as I cannot afford the parking fees. I haven't travelled this way for years. The day is cold. The taxi pulls up beside me on the main road; none of the windows are open. Inside, the people are wrapped in one another's scarves and coats, so close are they sitting to one another. It smells like porridge and hot breath. In Town the taxi drops us off near the train station. The stretch of paving that separates the train station from the taxi rank was empty only a few years ago, but now it is covered in uniform rows of stalls where Nigerian and Congolese women braid hair and their husbands sell phone accessories and sunglasses. I have lived in Cape Town my whole life, have been to Town many, many times, but on this day I am treated like a foreigner. My auburn hair and fair skin stand out. A man trying to sell me a fake pair of Ray-bans asks me where I am from.

'Here. Cape Town,' I say.

'And before that, sister?'

'Cape Town. I was born here.'

He laughs, insisting, 'But sister, tell me, what about your father? Where is he from?'

'From Cape Town. His whole life. He was born here too. We were born in the same hospital... And you? Where are you from?'

'Zimbabwe.'

'And your father?'

We both laugh at my question, but then the man frowns and replies, 'That's it, sister. We don't know who our fathers are. They could be from anywhere. Fathers are the big mystery of the world.'

I nod, though I don't really understand what he means. I know who my father is and where he is from. I have his birth certificate, his written records, photographs and the family trees he drew up. He is not a man whose origins are a mystery to me.

I walk on. The road is steep and I feel very small; the buildings lean over me, people stare.

Juliano and I get engaged without fanfare or announcements. The process is seamless, unsurprising. We have known that we will marry from very early on. 'Marry me,' he says as we lie in bed in the dark. 'Yes,' I reply and it is done. For a long time we tell no one. It is not a secret, but it feels somehow too personal to be made the property of others just yet. Though, for days afterwards I play with my mother's rings, trying them on, rehearsing as I did when I was a girl.

The process of my parents' engagement was different from ours – drawn out, painful, yet in the end, simple. When my father saw my mother on her first day of teaching, he knew that he would marry her. She wore pink suede shoes and had shapely legs from her time as an athlete, and looked away shyly whenever he spoke to her. Her English was bad, his Afrikaans was worse, yet they were able to communicate. The first time that he proposed to my mother, nine months after meeting her, my father first announced to his family and friends that he would be an engaged man that evening. At home he asked his mother to prepare a celebratory meal and he had plans for the party that would soon follow. When he returned later, alone, the food was already cold on the table.

My mother had felt that she was too young, and wasn't certain that marrying an English man was a good idea. Their backgrounds were so different. Many of her older relatives still harboured resentment about the Boer War. So my mother fled. She went to teach in Robertson, and when my father continued to visit her on Sundays, she fled further to Port Elizabeth. They wrote to one another regularly and he sent her postcards from his overseas travels. None of these survive.

Once a year for the following six years my father renewed his marriage proposal. He had no other girlfriends or lovers. He waited. Always my mother said no. Then, one long weekend when my father was visiting my mother in Port Elizabeth, he casually pointed at a house in the real estate pages of a newspaper, saying that he liked it. She disagreed; their house should be larger, have more rooms for the children. 'Does that mean you want to marry me?' he asked with surprise. 'Yes,' she replied. 'I suppose so.' Neither was afterwards able to remember in what language the exchange took place; by that time they were fluent enough in one another's languages.

I do not yet wear Adriana's ring that has been set aside for my engagement, though in quiet moments Juliano and I refer to one another as husband and wife. At night we sleep holding hands.

Downstairs Juliano is making coffee. The smell fills the apartment; there are no windows open. I pull the duvet over my nose and breathe through my mouth. I will sleep again, waiting until he leaves for work before I go downstairs and use the bathroom.

It is not him that I am avoiding. It is daylight and being awake and this damn book which I have grown to hate. Since returning from Brazil, I have written almost nothing. I wake each day with a sense of dread that I foster until I am unable to do anything. I lie on the couch and watch reality TV shows. When people ask me how the book is going, I tell them that I am in a 'thinking phase' or I just say 'it's fine'. I am tired of having to think of my father every day in this way. Of having to trawl through the past and imbue everything with meaning. The truth is that I had a difficult relationship with my father. Look at photos of the two of us. We are identical. Our personalities match each other's. We fought because we were the same in many ways.

How foolish it seems now, this memory of the first disappointment. I am seven years old and working my way through the Famous Five series. I try to have a discussion with my dad about them, only to have him admit he cannot remember the plots, and that anyway, he was more of a Secret Seven fan. This is worse than a disappointment. This is an unforgivable betrayal. I am furious, heartbroken. How can my father, who knows everything, who is right about everything, not know this – this in particular, this which matters so much to me. For half an hour I carry books to him, 'Don't you remember this part, Daddy?' At last he yells out, 'Good God, Karen, I read them 30 years ago! Why would I care about them now?' I storm off in a rage. Worse still, I know that he and my mother are laughing about me behind my back. In the garden I tear roses off my father's precious bushes. I tell myself that I will never forgive him. Not for this. Not for this failure to be what I want him to be. That is the worst disloyalty.

For six months I work as an outdoor activity instructor at Fairthorne Manor, an 111-acre estate near a small village called Botley in the south of England. I teach activities such as archery, abseiling, kayaking and orienteering to children, mostly those with special needs. They come in groups for a few days at a time. One boy, Alan, is autistic. He does not speak, cannot speak. He sits with his teacher the whole time and isn't able to take part in any of the activities. After his days at the Manor, he draws a picture which his mother posts to me. There is a letter K at the bottom of the page, in the middle is a giant red circle with stick-like arms coming out of the sides. I have pictures similar to these at home. Pictures I drew of my parents and my sister. My dad kept some of them. His face a circle blotted out by the fuzz that indicates a beard. Without language, this is how we mark down the moments and people that matter to us. A record of significance, sketched out in lines we are not always able to tame. I am flattered by Alan's picture of me, but also unsettled. Something about its sparseness comes too near to what I am. I am 18 years old. There is very little about myself that hasn't been moulded for me. I don't amount to much that I can say is my own.

Despite the lengthy interview process, the position at Fairthorne Manor is only a voluntary one. Along with 30 South Africans, New Zealanders and Australians, I get board and lodging in the manor house, a small room that sleeps three, and 40 pounds a week pocket money. The pounds go straight into beer on the weekends. It takes 15 minutes of brisk walking through a forested, unlit driveway to reach the road, another 20 to get to the village with its three pubs, off-licence and convenience store. Mostly we work on Saturdays, but afterwards we stay in the pubs until they close. Sundays we sleep off our hangovers and tell each other that next Sunday we should go on a day trip, but we rarely do. When we get given the Easter weekend off, the New Zealanders take a few extra days and go to Greece. Some of the Australians go to a surfing spot along the rugged English coast, coming back with colds and frozen toes. I take two weeks' worth of beer money that I have managed to save and go to Salisbury for two nights on my own.

I am not afraid of travelling alone. I am going to Salisbury because of Thomas Hardy, and, like Hardy's protagonists, I am a loner. My father gave me matching Penguin Classics editions of three of Hardy's novels when I was 12. I was too young, perhaps, to have a full understanding of their content, but it was the language that I fell in love with, the bleakness, the earthiness of it and the author's focus on landscape. At the time *Far From the Madding Crowd* was my favourite, followed by *Jude the Obscure*, while *Tess of the D'Urbervilles* completely eluded me. I could not understand the behaviour of the characters nor the consequences of their behaviour. Why did Angel abandon Tess hours after their marriage and why did she accept it so readily? Why was it Alec that she killed? Surely if murder had to be committed, she should have murdered Angel. Alec had never hidden who or what he was. But perhaps what confused me the most was the matter of ancestry. Tess's father learns that the Durbeyfields are descended from the noble D'Urberville line. Yet Tess's attempt to engage with that ancestry results in her rape by Alec and the death of her illegitimate baby. In the end, as she tries to flee that past, she and Angel rest at Stonehenge, where she recognises her mother's low ancestry in the surrounding fields and at last feels a sense of belonging; she is at home. The 'useless ancestors' are forgotten, they are nothing to her; 'not a thing of all that had been theirs did she retain but the old seal and spoon'; heirlooms from their noble past. The D'Urberville seal becomes an image of another life, something outside of hers. How is she able to remove herself from that past so easily?

I go to Stonehenge as a pilgrimage, to try and locate that something that I have always missed in *Tess of the D'Urbervilles*. For years I have envisioned this moment. How

I would approach the mammoth uprights, place my hand on them, and in that touching all would be clear. But Stonehenge is a disappointment. The structure is smaller than I had thought it would be. Because of a recent foot-and-mouth scare, the law requires visitors to stand on a straw path at a distance from the actual stones. I might as well be looking at a postcard. The wind is icy, the damp straw soaks through my shoes. I am cold and bored. In the distance cars pass on the road that cuts across the green landscape. I walk away and enter the gift shop. Near the counter are fridge magnets of family crests. I spot Jennings and begin to reach out for it. I will buy it for my father.

Only two hand-drawn originals exist of the Jennings family crest. Both were drawn by my father – one for each of his daughters. My sister's copy shows a blue background with a diagonal green strip within which is a rolled-up scroll. Above lies a wolf, though it could just as easily be a dog or a fox. Its tongue is sticking out and is slightly forked. Below, a red banner bears the motto FACTA NON VERBA. In my copy, the blue and red are replaced by purple and green, and the scroll is open. The wolf is facing the other way and the motto now reads VERBA NON FACTA. How strange, looking at them all these years later, strange that I did not notice these differences before.

At the age of ten I was given a school project to do regarding my family. It was the same project that my sister had done two years previously. I was expected to trace my family tree as far back as possible and then write a narrative about my ancestors. When I brought home the piece of paper outlining the assignment and showed it to my father, he folded it carefully and put it in his breast pocket. I did not see that piece of paper again for a week or more, during which time my father sat at the breakfast-room table trawling through an old picnic basket of photos and writing furiously on sheets of loose paper. He borrowed my sister's project and used it as a reference, even cutting out photocopied photos from its pages. On the night before the project was due, my father sat me down, presenting me with a booklet complete with photographs, family tree and coat of arms. He made me read the narrative out loud to him. There was a Portuguese sailor who had jumped ship upon arrival at the Cape. He had lived on the slopes of Table Mountain, eating root tubers and fighting off leopards. There were war heroes, film stars and inventors. A can-can dancer. A tortured artist. A wandering poet. It was a family comprised of people that any-one would be proud to be related to. In many of these ancestors I recognised parts of myself. For years to come, I carried that recognition and the people of my history with me in all my ac-tions and thoughts.

But the fridge magnet crest in the gift shop is not the crest that I know. It bears a knight's helmet, three pointed things that might be hats or towers or anything at all. It does not in any way resemble the ones my father drew. I don't know what to do. I go outside again. Stonehenge is so small. A tiny thing that may as well not even exist for all it has brought me. In my pocket I have only 14 pounds left. I take a pound coin and dial home from a pay phone. They will all be at the house having Easter Sunday lunch: my parents, sister, Ouma, Oupa, Granny and Aunty Kathleen. The wind howls around my head, whistling in the receiver as my father answers. He is surprised and pleased to hear from me, but I begin to scold him. 'What is this?' I say, describing the fridge magnet. 'Why is the Jennings coat of arms so different from our own?'

He laughs, 'But my girl, I thought you knew. I just made it up.'

'Why?'

'For your school projects. All of that stuff in the projects – I just made it up. To make them more interesting.'

'But Daddy, I lived my life by those people. I thought they were real.'

'Well, girl, then you've been wasting your time because they didn't exist.'

'What am I supposed to do now?' I ask.

He laughs again, surprised that I am so upset by something he hasn't given any thought to in years. 'Go sightseeing,' he tells me. 'There is a wonderful place nearby called Old Sarum. Go there and forget about this. It doesn't matter.'

I am irritated, angry. I want to be unforgiving and so I am. 'You're a liar,' I say before putting the phone down.

After his return from Russia, my father began to spend a small portion of each day compiling a brief family history; a true history this time, or as true as it could be. On Christmas Day he gave my sister and I a copy each. He had entitled it *Who Do You Think We Are*, having been particularly inspired by the BBC show of a similar name. I read my copy after a quiet Christmas lunch. By that time only Ouma was still alive out of the old people, and we had lunch more as an obligation to her than anything else. In the pages of that account, I learnt that the history of the Jennings-Leibbrandt-De Wet clan is one of feuding, bitterness, spite and misery. There is little in it that is comforting, and hardly anyone that one might be proud to name as a relative. It is not surprising then that my father fabricated a family for our projects. When I asked him about it, my father said that the process of writing about his family was like a bad dream that would not let him wake up; as with James Joyce's Stephen Dedalus, history was a nightmare from which he could not escape.

The story of the Jennings name begins in Ireland, though by the Middle Ages Jenningses were living in Worcestershire, the county where my great-grandfather Edwin Jennings was born on 21 August 1892. It is this man in particular who is an ancestor to be ashamed of. An ancestor useless as Tess's, and like hers too, best forgotten.

Edwin came to South Africa in the first decade of the twentieth century, not yet 18 years of age. Like many young men, he had come to seek his fortune in the post-Boer War colony, hoping for opportunities that England could not offer to its many unemployed. From Cape Town he made his way to Worcester, drawn by a town whose name echoed that of his home county. There he found a job as an electrician for the South African

Railways, and worked at maintaining the electric lines from Cape Town to Matjiesfontein. Within a year he had met and married Petronella Wahl, an illiterate Dutch girl, who had left school aged eight so that she could care for her family after her mother's death. Over the following years Edwin and Petronella had six children, the first, Frederick, being born in 1912. He was followed by Laetitia Martha (known as Pearl), Vincent Charles (known as Ginger), Richard Edwin (my grandfather), Kathleen Margaret and May, who only lived for two days.

Later the family left Worcester and moved to Salt River where Edwin had a job at the Railway Works. Frederick entered the Works aged 15 as an apprentice boilermaker. On Boxing Day of 1930, just turned 18, he drowned at Woodstock beach – a beach that does not exist anymore, the land having been reclaimed as Cape Town grew. Pearl left school at the age of 13 and worked as a matchbox packer at the Lion Match Company in Salt River. Ginger did stand-up comedy routines during the intervals at the cinema, before becoming a post office clerk and, later, an insurance salesman. Richard joined Ginger in the post office and again in insurance.

In the hard economic times of the 1920s and 30s it was expected that their money would be handed over to their father. He gave them a small amount of spending money from their wages. With the additional income, Edwin took himself on day trips into Town. He had no car since his affiliation with the railway meant that he could ride for free across the colony. At Cape Town station he would alight from the carriage and walk to Garlicks in Adderley Street. There he had the meal of the day at the department store's restaurant. For two slices of buttered bread, roast meat, potatoes, two vegetables and a dessert he paid one pound and sixpence. At home the family ate what they could grow in the garden and whatever meat Edwin had decided was affordable on the day. This he bought himself. Having worked out that government loaves were less expensive than the cost of baking bread at home, he gave his wife a small allowance with which to buy it from the corner store.

The government bread was bitter and rough, eaten with slices of penny polony and tomato sauce, all carefully meted out by Edwin, who ruled everything with a fist of iron. Petronella did the best that she could with the ingredients available to her. She served her family Irish stew, bean stew, cabbage stew, vegetable soup, marrowbone soup; not one dish distinguishable from the next.

There was nothing beautiful about her by this time. She was large, silent, always tired or ill. She did not speak unless it was to agree with her husband. On her face she nursed a reddish ulcer that grew over the years to fill an entire cheek. Edwin called it her cancer, and when bruises of his own making would appear beside it, he claimed it was the cancer spreading. With two children dead and a domineering husband, Petronella found comfort in nothing. She sat in the kitchen, lay on her bed. She hid her face from others, going nowhere but the garden or the corner shop for bread. Even church they rarely attended. Edwin resented having to put money in the collection plate.

The old man found no joy in the presence of his grandchildren. To him they were a nuisance, noisy, hungry, a waste of money. When my father visited during the holidays, Edwin would send him into the garden to play, no matter the weather. My father stood in the garage doorway, hiding from the rain. From there he looked at the green tool chest, the equipment covering the walls. He'd been told not to set foot inside the garage, and so he never did, not even when his own father tried to coax him inside to look at a wooden shelf he had made as a teenager.

Outside the Stonehenge Visitor Centre, the parking lot is filling up. Three large tour buses have arrived. Middle-aged American couples stand in groups talking loudly. It is the last day of their ten-day tour and they are tired, having just come from Bath, and needing to reach London by teatime. I hear a man saying, 'Honey, I'll take the photo, you go to the shop and see what you can find for the kids.'

A couple with two small girls in matching outfits and I are the only ones who board the bus to Old Sarum. The noise of the hundreds of milling people at Stonehenge begins to fade. All around the land is flat and green. I have no idea what Old Sarum is and so, as the bus deposits us some minutes later near what appears to be nothing more than a flat green hilltop, I try not to be surprised or disappointed. Two banks protect the hilltop, with a dry moat in between them. I walk across the moat on a long wooden bridge. Beneath me the grass is greener than any I have seen before. Wood and rock and green are the only things that surround me. I have come to the beginning of time. Upon the hilltop are the relics of buildings, not much more than lines of gathered rock. And yet it is beautiful. I feel more welcome, more at peace here than I did earlier.

On a small plaque, I read that this is the original site of Salisbury, a site more than 5,000 years old. By turns occupied and abandoned, it began as an Iron Age fort, then a Roman fortress and finally a Norman castle. In the early thirteenth century the hilltop became too small for the growing population, and feuding between the garrison and clergy resulted in a new site being chosen for the cathedral, two miles away. The old cathedral was taken apart and the materials used in the construction of the new. So too, the castle walls and other buildings were reconstituted in New Sarum, and Old Sarum was left to the wind and grass.

The name Sarum was not used until after the hilltop had been abandoned, and even then it resulted from an error. The Romans had called their hilltop town Sorbiodoni and later the Domesday Book records it as Sarisberie. The latter was abbreviated to Sa in registers. It would have been easy for a spot or extra flourish of the quill to be mistaken for an r – shorthand for the suffix rum. The error persisted, with the result that Salisbury had two names. To this day it is still officially known as New Sarum.

In his poem, 'De Translatione Veteris Ecclesie Saresberiensis et Constructione Nove' (The Translation of Old Salisbury

Cathedral and Construction of the New), written in the thirteenth century, the poet Henry D'Avranches describes Old Sarum as 'a windy, rain-swept place without flowers or birds... the bare chalk dazzled the eyes... There was a shortage of water, and a tiring climb to the top of the hill.' D'Avranches is right about the wind. My eyes water. My cheeks and nose are numb with the cold of it. But the chalk has long since been covered by green grass, and birds make their homes in the ruins of the old city. Below the castle remains, on a flat section of land, lies the outline of the former cathedral. From it one can look out over the lush fields and see the spire of the new cathedral towering over the landscape.

The castle itself is nothing more than rocks, none of them original. These are manufactured ruins. Rough stone walls have been resurrected where the castle once stood. They are modern-day trimmings, erected to represent the remains of something long since gone.

It is here, within the space marked out by these stones, that Eleanor of Aquitaine would have been imprisoned by her husband Henry II. It had been a fruitful marriage, bearing eight children, five of them sons. But Henry was never constant and it is reported that soon after their marriage, in the grounds of their castle at Woodstock, Eleanor saw the king walking with the end of a ball of silk caught on his shoe. Knowing it was not her silk, her suspicions were aroused, and she shadowed him to a maze in the park, where he disappeared. Later she returned to search the maze and found a door half hidden by the thicket. She opened it and followed a long underground passage, which led to a lodge in a remote part of the forest. Here Eleanor found a very beautiful lady engaged in embroidery with the silk she had seen on her husband's shoe. This was Rosamund Clifford, her husband's lover. Eleanor is said never to have forgiven her husband for his betrayal.

Wanting to be free from him and have power in her own right, she incited two of her sons to revolt against their father and demand Aquitaine as theirs to rule with their mother.

105

Despite her support and the addition of her own troops, the battle was lost. For her part in the revolt, Henry had her arrested and locked up in various castles until his death 16 years later. When Eleanor died at the age of 82, she had survived most of her children and seen three of her sons on the throne of England.

Where I sit behind the castle walls to rest and get out of the wind, I find a small packet of Easter eggs lodged between two stones. I look around and see nobody nearby. Perhaps they belong to the family from the bus. I am hungry and lonely and cold. I eat the eggs, hiding the empty packet in my jacket pocket afterwards.

In 1955, my grandfather, Richard Jennings, opened a hardware store in a small complex off Belvedere Road in Claremont. As he was working full time for the SA Eagle Insurance Company, he arranged that his father, who had recently retired, would work in the shop from Mondays to Fridays. But Edwin was mean, miserable, rude to the customers. Soon he had driven away any potential shoppers and within eight months the shop was losing money and my grandfather was badly in debt. The store had to be closed and my grandmother had to go back to work as a typist in order to help pay off their debts. The first payment went to Edwin, who demanded his full wages for the time that he had 'wasted in that bloody place'.

When Petronella died, Edwin stayed on in the house, his miserliness amplified by loneliness. He switched off the electricity, he only flushed the toilet once a day, he begged the daily newspapers from his neighbours, and stopped buying toilet paper because he could use the old newspapers instead. With time it became clear that he could no longer look after himself, but none of his children would take the old man in. He sold the house and lived in a succession of boarding houses, suspicious of everyone, unkind wherever he went. No boarding house would keep him beyond a few weeks, then he would go to his children for a while, though he hated them all. Each in their turn had been excluded from his will, and when the old man died, Ginger found more than 40 copies of it, each explaining in detail why so-and-so would be receiving nothing.

My father often spoke of the day that his mother, Trixie, threw the old man out of her house. Edwin had gone to town that day to eat his department store lunch at Garlicks. When Trixie came home after five o'clock from her typist's job, she prepared dinner. The old man, instead of saying he wasn't hungry, glared at the food, threw his cutlery across the table and shouted, 'I can't eat this filth. Have you never learnt to cook?' There was silence at the table. Trixie turned to her husband and spoke very quietly and slowly, 'Dick, will you go and pack your father's cases. I want him out of this house in 30 minutes.' She then picked up her knife and fork and continued eating, nodding to my father and Jean to do the same. Edwin began screaming at her, but my grandfather packed the old man's bags and drove him to Pearl, leaving him standing on her doorstep. Pearl immediately phoned Kathleen who also refused to take her father. Kathleen was the only one who had ever seemed to care for the old man, but her love for him was limited to the times that she wanted something from him. Edwin spent that night at Pearl's flat and the next day he was moved to a boarding house in Rosebank. There he remained until his death three months later, seeing no one, going nowhere, writing and re-writing his will.

From Old Sarum it is a two-mile walk back to Salisbury. I walk through green fields and small lanes, the giant spire of the cathedral guiding me. In a field about a mile from the city, I stop to watch some boys flying their kites. The kites dip and rise in the wind, I can hear the whoosh of their movements through the air. In a far corner of the field, an old man is strolling. His right hand grips a walking stick. With his left he is shielding his eyes from the wind. A kite drops low, just above him. He is startled by the sound it makes and stumbles, falling to his knees. By the time I reach him, he has managed to pull himself up on his walking stick.

'Just look at that,' he says, pointing to his muddied knees. 'All over my Sunday best.'

He seems unsteady and so I offer to walk him home.

'It's not far,' he tells me. 'Just across the field and down the lane.' He asks where I am from and when I say South Africa he replies, 'Oh I thought it might be America. We have ties to America, you know.'

I don't know, but I nod my head.

'Yes, only loosely you know. Made my grandfather blow his brains out that whole thing over there.'

'What thing?' I ask, confused.

The man smiles, shakes his head and hand at the same time. 'Oh, never mind that now. I can't remember it all anyway. Now, tell me, have you been to the museum yet?'

'No, just to Stonehenge and Old Sarum.'

'Waste of time, my dear, waste of time. It's all in the museum, you know. All of it. My grandfather, Richard Fowler – this is the other one, now, the one who didn't shoot himself – this one, well, he founded that museum from a collection of things he found in the drain.'

'In a drain?'

'Oh yes. Salisbury used the same drainage system since the Middle Ages and all manner of things got lost in there over the centuries. When they installed a new system in the 1850s the workmen found over a thousand items. Keys, jewellery, religious objects hidden during the Reformation, a chess piece that is seven hundred years old! Seven hundred years, just think of that. So my old granddad, he took it all, named it the Drainage Collection and opened a museum.'

'It sounds interesting,' I tell him.

'It is, it is. But there's more to it than that. There's also the preserved body of a rat that he found in the skull of the Earl of Salisbury when he opened his tomb. Imagine that, a rat eating your brain away. But the best things are the Giant and Hobnob. My great great great – oh, I don't know how many times – grandfather built them for processions in the fifteenth century. He would carry the Giant – 14 feet high it was – and in front of him his brother went as Hobnob, a horse with a mouth that opens, with teeth made from hobnails, and Hobnob would clear the crowds. There would be Morris dancers and a devil and fools and a man with a drum making the sound of the Giant's footsteps. So, you see, all these relics from my ancestors are all still living there, in the museum.'

'That's wonderful,' I reply. 'To have all of that history, and it's all right here on your doorstep.'

We reach a small cottage with a hurdle fence. An old lady with short white hair is coming out of the gate. 'Ned,' she calls, 'I've been getting worried. Where have you been?'

He laughs and points at his knees, 'I fell and then I met this young lady and we've been talking.'

'Look at the state of you. Go on inside and wash up. Look at your hands!'

The old man smiles at me and waves goodbye as he walks slowly up the path to the front door. The woman comes up to me and says, 'Thank you for being so kind. I hope he didn't bore you too much with his stories. He can go on and on. But you mustn't pay them any mind, my dear. These stories, they're not true. He's an orphan, you know, orphaned in the war, the first one, and so he likes to make up a past for himself. I never believe half the things he says, but it's worse now he's old. One day he's descended from kings, the next from bishops or mayors. We're not even from this area. We only moved here five years ago.'

My face must show my concern because she takes my hand and pats it, 'But you mustn't worry, my dear, he's quite harmless. And all the facts are true. He has a good head for facts. It's just the rest that isn't true.'

'Well, go on then, enjoy your day,' she says, releasing my hand.

By the time I reach the museum, it has closed. I am leaving Salisbury early the following morning. I will not have a chance to see the museum and the items that this man has used to create a history for himself.

The Jenningses do not speak of things that are unpleasant or relate to emotion in any way. It is for this reason that I did not know of Linda's existence until her death in 1993. My sister and I were told to write Aunty Kathleen letters of sympathy and then we all drove to Pinelands, taking with us flowers and food. Uncle Vic had been dead for a year already, so it was only Aunty Kathleen and her old dog, Holly, living in the house.

Linda was their second child, born in 1958, with Down's syndrome. At her birth, the doctor had taken her away and advised that she be put in a home. Kathleen did not ever see Linda, and she was never spoken of, though I was told that in the last decade of his life, Vic began to visit her in the care home that is still there, off the main road in Plumstead. Their only other child, Derek, died in a car accident the year that I was born. He had been a newlywed and they did not ever forgive his bride for remarrying several years later. For as long as I can remember Aunty Kathleen would phone me on my birthday, and even when I was young, she would tell me that I must have my babies early. 'Have them all before you turn 25,' she would say every year, as though by repeating herself she could make it happen. That was the only reference, perhaps, to Linda that she ever made to me, and it was meant kindly, I am sure, though she carried her resentment with her like a badge, and I am told that when I was born she said to my father, 'You must be disappointed to have another girl.'

Linda had no funeral that I know of, and my only recollection of that day is Aunty Kathleen's face drawn tight with bitterness as she sat on her floral couch, Holly at her feet. Linda was not mentioned beyond once or twice after that day, and never in Aunty Kathleen's presence.

One Sunday afternoon some months after Aunty Kathleen had died, my grandmother was telling me about Edwin, what an awful man he was and how Kathleen had carried the man's bile in her veins. She said that when Linda was born the old man had put the blame on my grandmother for the girl's condition, maintaining that she had passed on the germs to Kathleen.

Germs, he claimed, that Trixie had been infected with from her mother, Anna, who had died from Parkinson's Disease. It was ignorance, of course, but it was malice too. Already strained relationships within the family became tenser.

When Pearl died she left no will. It was ordered by the Master of the Court that Pearl's closest relations would inherit and share everything equally among them – therefore the estate would be divided in equal portions among Richard, Ginger and Kathleen. But Kathleen had other ideas. She claimed everything for herself – all the furniture, all the jewellery, all the money, the car, every item in the house. She explained to her brothers that it was her due and that Pearl had loved her more. Accusations flew between the siblings, references to the germs, to how Ginger and Richard had not cared for their father when he was in need, and other allegations that my grandmother would not or could not remember when I asked her. The siblings did not speak to one another again. When her brothers died, more than a decade apart, Kathleen attended the funeral services, but did not go to the teas afterwards.

It was only some time after my grandpa Richard's death that my parents began to try to bring the family together again. However, there was always a sense of unease, everyone was very careful not to say the wrong thing, to make no mention of the past. As children, my sister and I were schooled in who or what we were allowed to refer to. Mostly we were quiet.

Within a few years, the Jennings family had been reduced to us four, my grandmother and Aunty Kathleen. There was no joy for us in Christmases and Easters; Aunty Kathleen sitting at the head of the table, droning on without pause. The last Christmas that they were both alive was in 2006. As usual my grandmother took up a position behind Kathleen, gripping her hands together behind the woman's throat, miming strangulation. She did this for our benefit, but for her own too. She had never been able to like her sister-in-law, perhaps never to forgive her either. Yet she cried when Kathleen died. It was the last link to a former life, a life of bitterness and feuding, but of love too, and family.

In Salisbury Cathedral close, I stroll for half an hour beneath the trees that flank its left side. I have already been through the cloisters and taken my turn to look at the Magna Carta in Charter House. But now I am restless. Above me, the branches of the trees do little to spare me the sight of the spire which has been at the edge of every view this whole day. The tallest in Britain, it dominates everything. No part of the local landscape is free from its presence. It is spectacular, unnatural, the cathedral itself too squat beneath such vastness. Under the weight of its shadow, I feel myself being crushed into something as flat as the stones that make up the path that surrounds the building. This building, centuries old, built by the hands of men who believed in something great, something beyond themselves, beyond past or future. Standing here, this morning's conversation with my father feels a hundred years away. Yet, in my pocket I have the crest that I saw at Stonehenge. I bought it after all, despite my anger at him. All day it has sat in my pocket, heavy as a rock.

Around the cathedral doors people have begun to gather. For some time they have been standing in groups of twos or threes, but at a signal, unheard, they have formed themselves into a line. The evening light has been dimming, so that when the cathedral doors are opened, a golden light pours out and over the waiting people. The dusk is made hollow by it; faces highlighted to a point where their features disappear. From where I stand, they are all same-faced, entering the cathedral as a single person with different clothing and movements.

Because I am cold, and perhaps a little tired of my own company, I join the queue. A man at the doors hands me a pamphlet – it is a special Easter service. Hymns and prayers are printed out for us on white paper that bears a line-drawing of the cathedral on the cover. The back of the pamphlet asks for donations to be made as we leave after the sermon. My pounds are dwindling rapidly. I doubt whether I will have enough to eat tomorrow. I should not have bought the crest.

I choose a chair towards the back. It is a lone seat, at the end of a row. Beside me a husband and wife stare silently at their pamphlets. The rest of the congregation is in silence too. When the priest mounts the pulpit, the wife nudges her husband, as though to silence him even further. The congregation is welcomed and told that there will be a special performance preceding the sermon as a celebration of this holy time. Beside the pulpit a temporary stage has been erected that is high enough to be visible to all reaches of the cathedral. In the centre, a bare-chested man begins to dance as discordant jazz music plays. His dance depicts a man in pain, a man dying. As he lies on the stage, a woman reads W.H. Auden's 'Funeral Blues' while Irish music plays and girls in green dresses dance around the fallen body. One of them paints a large red cross on the man's back before helping him to his feet. He is Jesus, resurrected. As he walks away from us, up the aisle, we are invited to stand and sing. I look at the pamphlet in my hand. The hymn is seven verses long. I mumble along with the first two. My stomach has begun to growl and I am tired. The hymn drags, the rhyme belaboured. Mid-way through the third verse, I turn away from the page in my hand and look, instead, at what surrounds me. Row upon row of people are mirrored in the vaulted ceiling; ribs of wood and stone that arc and flow in a steady wave over our heads. The aisles are lined with lights that reflect off the pale walls, the tall windows, forming shadows on the ceiling. Walls teem with movement, the ceiling ripples forward. All this great building is alive around me.

As I stand, the organ's solemn hymn vibrating through the floor, I am reminded of a plaque I saw earlier in the cathedral grounds. It bore a quote from T.S. Eliot's *Four Quartets*:

We die with the dying:
See, they depart, and we go with them.
We are born with the dead:
See, they return, and bring us with them.

I have the poem with me, in my bag. It is an affectation, something I have done for years; carrying a poetry anthology with me wherever I go, scrawling notes in it that I imagine matter. When the hymn is finished and the sermon begins, I reach into my bag and withdraw the book. The poem continues, 'A people without history/ Is not redeemed from time, for history is a pattern/ Of timeless moments.'

Again I look at the walls in movement. I think of the places I have visited today, of the ways they have been constructed. In Salisbury, old stones were used to build a new cathedral that is still standing 800 years later, while at Old Sarum new stones have been used to resurrect the ruins of an old city. It is difficult to separate what is alive from what is dead, what is false from what is true. We are all guilty of it: dismantling the past, trying to create something new, something we consider to be an improvement. Even in this book there are memories I have created from the rubble of others.

PART FIVE: REMEMBERING THE DEAD

THE SOLDIER

My stay in Arnhem in the Netherlands coincides with the 69th anniversary of the battle of Arnhem, when British and Polish troops were sent to wrest key bridges across the Nederrijn from German forces. The attempt was unsuccessful and over 2,000 Allied soldiers lost their lives in the nine-day battle. The First Airborne Division alone was reduced by three-quarters. The city is full of memorials to victims of the war. In shops, on buildings are pictures, books and statues that mark their passing. A series of comics has been drawn, bringing the battle to life in vivid colour. I meet the author one Saturday in the bookshop below the apartment that I am staying in. He tells me that a Jewish man hid in the attic of the building for three years during the war. He points out the commemorative plaque on the bookshop exterior and the small display in the shop that remembers this man. When I return to the apartment, I notice the door to the attic for the first time. One of the keys on the bunch that I have been given opens the door. The attic is dark and musty. It holds no memory of human presence but for the piles of artwork stacked against the walls; a storage place used by the foundation that is hosting me.

Now that I know of a man's having been confined here for three years, I feel trapped by the apartment. I go for walks more regularly. All over the city I find monuments to the dead. In Kerkplein the entire six-centuries-old Eusebius church has been transformed into a memorial. Destroyed during the war, the church has been restored and now boasts an elevator that will take visitors to the top of the 93-metre-high spire. From there, the whole city is visible, spread out as evenly as a map. From one of four sets of windows the 'bridge too far' can be seen spanning the Nederrijn, where many men lost their lives. Each year there are services held at the bridge to commemorate the fallen. They are attended by descendants from all across Europe. The dead are not forgotten.

We lost no family in the war. My grandfather volunteered and joined up with the Cape Town Highlanders and was issued with the full kit. However he was declared unfit for combat because of a kidney complaint. He was placed on Home Guard duty and spent the war guarding military installations like the Castle. Victor fought in North Africa, and Ginger was seconded to the Entertainment Corps. William Cloete, who would marry Pearl, and Albert Carr, who would marry Peggy, my grandmother's sister, also served up north.

We have no tales of loss, no letters or other memorabilia. We have only a faded photograph, folded in half, that my grandmother kept amongst her things. A few years before her death she showed the photo to us. On it were three young soldiers in putties and pith helmets. They are leaning against a rock, jungle behind them. The man in the middle has blond hair, a proud smile. It looks as though the others, shorter, darker, have taken their lead from him. Their faces are comical as they try to match his stern expression. It is the middle soldier that my grandmother met at a canteen in Cape Town in 1941 when his ship docked at the harbour. She had been unmarried then and had let the young soldier kiss her. When he arrived in India he sent her this photograph of himself and his mates. After that he went to Burma and she did not hear from him again.

At the top of the Eusebius church tower the elevator doors open and I wait for a family of five to get off before I enter. As the doors close, I hear the British accent of the father. 'From here I can show you where he died,' he tells his teenage son. His two daughters, younger, run to the set of windows and shriek at the height.

There is little more for me to see in this vast memorial to the fallen. The large interior of the church is empty but for plaques, listing names and ranks of soldiers who fought in the war. Further in there are carved stone slabs decorating the resting places of the long-dead. A damaged and faded wooden slat bears a painted map of the church floor, showing in small rectangles where important people from Arnhem's past have been buried. Above, high ceilings bear an installation depicting paratroopers falling out of a white sky.

In the furthest corner, near to where a pulpit might have once stood, is a small hole in the ground, no bigger than a man-hole cover, and an iron staircase leading into darkness. I call across the great hall to a man who is sweeping, asking whether I am allowed below. He says yes and asks me to wait until he has switched on the lights. The stairs are steep and shake under my weight. They lead into a brief series of rubble-filled caves that I clamber over and through until I reach a small precipice. Below me is an area of excavated earth. About four or so pits are visible, and in them, lying as though recently discovered, are skeletons. I try to take photos, but the dim light causes the images to blur so that it looks like a single skeleton in motion.

As I leave the strange crypt, I stop at a marble-carved grave-stone. On it are depicted two bodies sharing a grave. The first image is of a woman in a long dress, beside her is a skeleton, its body and clothing decomposing. One of the cupids bordering the pair was damaged in the war and has no face; it stares at the couple, eyeless, its features seemingly melted.

The pink armchair is gone, replaced by a larger, more comfortable one that my mother doesn't want anymore. It used to be in the front lounge of the big house; the lounge that we used only at Christmases, Easters and on the day my father died. There is a tear under the left armrest from when Juliano and I forced it into the back of my car. He likes to sit in it in the evenings while I stretch out on the couch.

I have spent the evening packing, preparing for a residency in Uganda, despite only recently having returned home from the Netherlands. I don't know what to take, what the weather will be like. Hot, I imagine. Now I lie on the couch, nervously trying to recall what went into the bag and what was discarded. From the cream-coloured armchair Juliano flicks through channels on the television. It is a Saturday night, there is nothing worth watching. But then a familiar face on the screen causes me to say, 'Stop on this one.' It is my great-uncle, Ginger Jennings, wearing a pair of white overalls and driving a car. I know this movie, have watched it once before with my father. It is *Lord Oom Piet*, written and directed by Jamie Uys in 1962.

The movie is supposed to be a comedy and tells the story of Oom Piet Kromhout of Kransberg, a staunch Afrikaner and National Party supporter. He is standing for election against his English neighbour, Sir David, who represents the United Party. The two farmers bicker about politics, while their teenage children, reminiscent of Romeo and Juliet, are secretly in love. To make matters worse, Oom Piet receives shocking news that he is, in fact, an English lord. This is terrible for a man who claims to be a thorough Afrikaner. When the news becomes public knowledge, it is certain that he will not win the election. The only solution to becoming a commoner again is to challenge a nobleman like Sir David to a duel, and lose. But how can Oom Piet lose to the man he wants to crush in the election, a man he despises?

The movie is ridiculous, offensive. It unashamedly fore-grounds the prejudices prevalent in South Africa at the time – English versus Afrikaans, white versus black, National Party versus United Party. I watch only for the few sightings of Ginger and for the scene that my father appeared in. He was 16 years old, given a job as an extra through Ginger's connections. Years ago my father and I watched this movie, going through a particular crowd scene as slowly as the video recorder would al-low so that we might catch a glimpse of him. My father thought he recognised his shirt – just the sleeve of it in the corner of the screen. I look again with Juliano, but see nothing. There is really no need to watch anyway. Ginger's voice was dubbed and his role cut in the editing room for reasons that my father told me but that I can no longer remember. I go to *Who Do You Think We Are*, thinking the answer might be in there, but I find very little beyond this paragraph:

Ginger had married Edith. He bought a house in Belvedere Road, Claremont and was just getting settled into married life, as an insurance underwriter and as a part-time comedian when his mother-in-law and sister-in-law moved in with them and they stayed with them until he died. Aileen, Edith's sister, was a spinster, who belonged to the ultra-strict religious sect called the Plymouth Brethren. In a dream the Lord appeared to her and told her NOT to marry the young man to whom she was engaged. He, according to my father who played in the same soccer team with him, was a really fine young man and would have made a good husband. Anyway, once he was dumped he started drinking to get over the rejection and this was reported to Aileen by others and she felt justified that she had dumped him 'as the sin had obviously been hidden in him all the time'. How they all lived in that three-roomed house with one tiny bathroom without irritation and arguments is amazing. How Ginger survived the sisters' dour assault on his jolly nature is beyond me.

121

I wake early the next morning, nervous about my trip, and switch on the television. The same movie is on, the channel featuring its programmes in a seemingly endless loop. I watch my great-uncle again, his voice out of synch with his lips.

'*Muzungu*,' the guard says outside the bank in Entebbe, 'please, it is necessary for me to see inside your bag.'

I open it wide.

'It is a Bible?' he asks of the book inside.

'No, a novel. Just a story book.'

'Ah, today you forgot your Bible, but tomorrow you will remember.'

It isn't unusual to be mistaken for a missionary when you are a *muzungu* – a foreigner; more specifically, a white foreigner. As with many African countries, Uganda has a long history of Christian missionaries coming to their land, bringing with them the word of God. Even when my presence in the country is not misinterpreted, there is a desire for people to speak to me of God.

'I see Him in your face,' one man tells me on the shores of Lake Victoria. He carries a rifle, wears a sweater over his uniform. All morning it has been raining, and now that it has stopped, the paths are puddled, the air warm with the smell of damp earth. A woman rakes wet leaves on wet grass. Birds sing. A boy in a boat is slowly paddling across the still water, while on a farther part of the shore, men are hammering, carrying, building something new. Midges swarm at disparate points in the landscape. A cloud hovers ever nearer; I swat it away and step aside. The man seems not to be bothered by them. 'Lake flies,' is all he says as he readjusts the rifle strap.

I make a point of not asking what the rifle is for. Across Uganda it is the same: riflemen, uniformed in various colours. Policemen, security guards, everywhere there is a man armed, guarding. But guarding against what I cannot say with any certainty. Perhaps, it speaks to the worst ideas we have of Uganda, of Africa as a whole even. Memories of dictators and coups and dismemberments. Violence and poverty are easy points to remember, especially of a continent that outsiders have tended to paint all one colour, which they consider as one place and people. Yet at no time do I feel threatened, afraid. I walk in the streets at night. I go everywhere alone. Very different from my life at home in Cape Town.

The man has his back to the lake, and behind him a monitor lizard emerges from the shallows and lies down on the ragged weeds that have washed up. 'Here,' he says, 'you see we love God.' He takes a worn paperback from his pocket. It is a children's book of scripture. 'We love God so much that we carry Him with us all day and He carries us.' This I have seen. On cars, on vans, boats and buildings, God's name abounds. Street cafés have faith-related names and one market stall I pass advertises Lord's milk at 2,000 shillings a litre. Churches have grandiose names that are proudly advertised on billboards and with flyers. Welcome Deliverance of Celestial Martyrs. The People's Only Christ the Saviour Church of Divinity. Born Again Reverence of the Word.

'God came to Uganda because we are poor. So he is very busy here. He loves us because we are poor and so we love him back and then even if we are poor we are rich, you understand? But for you it is easier. Already you are rich and you are *muzungu*, so you are closer.'

I ignore the reference to being rich, asking only, 'You mean closer to God?'

A cloud of lake flies has formed around me, they will not move, coming back as soon as my hands stop parting them.

'To God and everything. Because you are American.'

'No. No, I'm South African. I have never even been to America. I'm African.'

'Hoohoo,' he laughs as though he doesn't believe me. 'African *muzungu*.'

Though it is a term used commonly by the people of Uganda and its neighbouring countries to refer to a white person, the word *muzungu* has become something of a commodity in recent decades and is employed as a device in the tourist trade. Vendors use it to charm their buyers, *boda-bodas* call to tourists to entice them onto their motorcycle taxis. Across the country children might be seen to shout, 'Bye-bye *muzungu*' and wait for a coin to be their reward. Derived from the Bantu '*wachizungu*', a person who wanders aimlessly, or the Kiswahili '*zungu*', which describes a person who spins around on one spot, the word has been used in various forms since the eighteenth century in reference to European explorers who came to the continent, searching for something they could not name, getting lost, yet walking on and on, seeking an unknown end.

I continue swatting. The flies hover and hover, ever increasing. The man watches.

'You are fearing, but you must not. When the rains come again they will die. Today we live with them. Tomorrow they are gone.'

Drive from Entebbe to Jinja any day of the week and watch as the city shrinks beside you, grows again, expands into Kampala, which dominates and then disappears. Pass by wooden huts, brick homes, ministries, schools. Cattle asleep in long grass, banana trees, children holding hands. Four goats tethered to one another on a patch of land that boys are using as a soccer field. The grass is played away. The goats pull in different directions. Buildings, painted red or yellow, advertising cellphone providers. A giant statue of a man in a loincloth touting clay-works, where bricks are made. Behind the wall they are piled, drying. Women balance bags of unknown things on their heads. A man pushes a bicycle, laden with five crates of soda bottles. *Boda-bodas* stand astride their motorbikes under trees, their coats hanging from branches. Wide-hipped mannequins wear cheap clothing; carpenters build vast bed-frames on the side of the road.

Then there are traffic lights, young men selling grasshoppers from trays, and a pause as the city demands traffic to slow down, acknowledging where it is. This is the end of things green; the beginning of cars, people, *boda-bodas*, taxis, buses, trucks, all moving at once towards different destinations. They all seem to have their own rules, yet no one collides. The motions are fluid, if not uniform, and we leave the city as easily as a lone boat on a wide expanse of water.

Far beyond Kampala, an hour later, the car stops at what appears to be a market. Roofed stalls sell fruit and vegetables and other types of food. It is hot and I have had one of my feet half out of the passenger-seat window since we left the city. At the car's approach onto the dirt beside the road, 50 or so men and women in numbered blue bibs rush at the car. They carry sodas, bottled water, woven bowls filled with bunches of small bananas hardly bigger than my thumb, long sticks threaded with some kind of black meat or the breast and thigh of a chicken. There is even an old lady offering carrots in plastic bags. They ambush the car, jostling. The driver buys two sticks of black meat, asks if I want some.

'No, thank you,' I tell him. 'I don't eat meat.'

'Ah, Miss *muzungu*,' he replies, 'you must not be fearing. In Uganda we have herbs you can take. They will heal you and then you will eat meat again.'

I am about to reply when I feel something on my foot that is still half out of the window. A man holding a bouquet of chicken-breasted sticks is touching the sole of my foot with one finger. He sees me watching, smiles broadly. '*Muzungu*,' he says and laughs, continuing to look at my foot as though it is something foreign to him. I pull it inside, place it on the floor. The man twists his head so that he can look down at my feet, watching them all the while as the driver finishes his skewers of meat. Others lean against the car, waiting for cars and buses to stop.

The trip has taken longer than I thought it would. I doze in the car, my feet sweating a wet patch into the rug on the floor. I dream that we are driving around the circle in Kampala where we stopped earlier this morning to make way for the deputy president and a cavalcade of cars, sirens blaring. In my dream we drive around the circle, on and on. My foot swells as we move, my toes enlarging until the whole car is engulfed, turned into a single foot that circles and circles.

The driver startles me awake. 'See Miss *muzungu*, the trees are darker here. That is the sign. That is how we know we are almost there.'

We make no stops at Jinja, going straight to the tourist attraction of the source of the Nile, which bubbles up from within Lake Victoria. I pay 10,000 shillings to enter the area and am introduced to Isaac. He will take me across the water to a small island from where I will be able to see the source, which is advertised by handwritten and printed signs alike along the winding road that leads from the ticket office down to the lake.

I am placed in a boat that is painted with the words God is Good. It tips and sways with my steps, but steadies as I sit. My lifejacket has no straps. It hangs loosely at my sides as Isaac points out cormorants, storks, an otter, fishermen with a net, and on a distant shore, a prison. At the small island, no bigger than a driveway, he helps me from the boat.

'The water is high today because of the rains,' he tells me, pointing at a wooden hut perched on the furthest end of the strip of land. 'Take off your shoes, please, and walk through the water, then you go through the shop, then out again. Then you will see the source of the Nile.'

I do as he says, walking carefully over slippery rocks, holding up my trousers, which threaten to get wet. The wooden hut is under water and smells of wet wood, damp cloth. It is dark inside. I peer dimly; it contains the same soapstone and wooden carvings, paintings and fabrics that any other stall might have.

'There is lots to buy here. I give you special price,' says a woman standing with her feet in the water. 'T-shirts, you see.' Gift shops in Uganda and all around east Africa tend to sell the same two T-shirts. MUZUNGU says the one. MY NAME IS NOT MUZUNGU says the other. They are jokes, aimed at tourists who will wear them while they travel and then occasionally back home for a conversation piece.

'I am not *muzungu*,' I say to the lady.

'Yes, this one,' she says, holding up a pink-coloured MY NAME IS NOT MUZUNGU T-shirt.

'No,' I say, 'no thank you.'

I exit the hut through the other door, directly into the lake. A round blue sign in the water identifies what is claimed to be the source of the Nile. I stand beside it, hold up my camera and take a photo of myself hastily as a noisy Indian family approaches, pushing me to the side. I lean against the wall of the gift shop, beneath a sign that warns of fines for urinating. I watch the water, unable to distinguish between Lake Victoria, the source or the Nile itself. All appears the same to me, water expanding out, north, south, east and west. I look down at my camera. The screen shows the photo I have just taken beside the blue sign. I aimed poorly. I am not in the frame. Only in the bottom right-hand corner, a strand of my hair, blowing, and in the distance, water and water.

After returning from Uganda, I find work for a fortnight, marking high school exam scripts six nights a week. The work is mindless and the hours take some adjusting to, but I enjoy the company of others and the sense of completion that accompanies the end of each box of marking. It does, however, mean that so soon after having been apart, Juliano and I are separated again. Other than Sundays, we see each other only in the brief moments when I climb into bed, waking him, and when he rises in the morning, waking me.

On the second Sunday we rise late. It is the day before my birthday, and despite a week of sun, we now find the sky grey, the wind fierce. I had wanted to go for a walk at Constantia Nek, but instead we choose to visit the harbour at Hout Bay and its market. The sea there is too cold to swim in, the sand is dirty, but the view is pleasant; the distant shores of the peninsula continuing southward, the harbour with its fishermen and seals. One of these men performs for tourists, placing the innards of fish between his teeth so that they dangle low enough that seals can reach up and take them. He will be harmed by this some day. The male seals are large, can be violent. We disapprove of what this man does, yet we watch from a distance. It is difficult not to be intrigued by these large bodies, moving clumsily as a wet sack.

Hout Bay is an isolated suburb, bordered by mountains on three sides, the ocean on the fourth. A signpost at Constantia Nek announces that you are entering the Republic of Hout Bay. It is no more than a joke, yet there is a sense of independence that isolation has brought to the place. It seems a world apart, a microcosm representing at once the past and present, a stark reminder of South Africa both before and after 1994, with its mix of wealthy white landowners, the coloured fishermen on the hangs of the mountain, and on the other side, near the winding road, the Imizamo Yethu informal settlement where black families live, making their money as domestics, gardeners, waiters.

The desire to oust the poor, the unsightly, is ever-present. Every year tensions arise, demonstrations are held, police are called. Hout Bay ratepayers want the informal settlement gone; they oppose proposals to allocate more land to the settlement. Twenty thousand people live on the 18 hectares of Imizamo Yethu. Their conditions are cramped, filthy. They have no plumbing, no roads, no way of making a living outside of Hout Bay's borders. Transport out of the suburb is too expensive, the distances far. So crime prevails in the affluent areas of the suburb. Houses are broken into. Cars are stolen. Once in a while vigilante groups burn the shacks that overflow their borders or beat up their inhabitants. Tensions persist with no sign of being resolved.

At the harbour I allow the excess of a birthday celebrated a day early to overwhelm me and order four scoops of gelato. We sit on a bench outside and look around us. The wind blows grains of sand into my ice-cream, but I eat it anyway. There are no fishermen on the rough water, only boats docked and young men walking their fighting dogs on rope leads along the harbour walls. Something as small as this – the taste of gelato, the smell of salt in the air – returns my father to me. It is as though he is sitting beside me, and I feel an urge to turn towards him and say hello.

Most days I give my father ice-cream where he lies in bed or is sitting in his chair. He can only eat a few spoonfuls at a time, but I slip it in with the protein shakes he has to take or I give him a small bowl of it when he says he doesn't want his breakfast. My father was a big man; he loved food. By now he is thin, the skin of his stomach hangs, his legs are too thin to carry him. The only thing he enjoys eating is ice-cream, everything else hurts or takes too much effort. His immune system is depleted from the chemotherapy and so he has developed thrush in his mouth, telling no one until we notice the strange way he has

130

begun to speak. Looking closer we find a swollen tongue, a white mouth specked with blood-red cracks.

In the evenings I lie beside him on the double bed and we watch from his collection of movies. Neither of us laughs at them, or if we do, we do so self-consciously, as though we shouldn't really be enjoying ourselves. He eats his ice-cream slowly as we watch. It has all but melted in the bowl. I tease him about it, and in my teasing I unleash in him a memory from his early years. He begins to tell me about a relative of his who ate slower than he was doing now.

Anna de Wet's brother, Christiaan, was known to everyone as Uncle Oomie because of the mix of Afrikaans and English that was spoken in his house. When his wife died, a nurse was hired to come and look after him and the house. This nurse was Milly. Her surname has been lost with time. She was a painfully thin, grey, drawn lady who rarely spoke. Yet there must have been something in her that appealed to Uncle Oomie because he eventually married her. Only afterwards did anyone discover that she had been married four times before, in each case to a widower that she had been nursing. Milly always wore black, in mourning for her dead husbands, and continued to do so when Uncle Oomie passed away. Her new family joked behind her back that she had murdered her husbands, but the truth is more likely that she was a lonely lady, looking for romance in the only place that she could find.

Milly continued to be invited to family get-togethers after Uncle Oomie's death, and she came readily, though it was a pain to have her present. She ate excruciatingly slowly. So slowly that everyone else would be eating their dessert while she was still busy on her soup. She would stay behind in the dining room, eating alone while the family retired to the lounge. When, at last, she was finished, she would take her plate through to the kitchen where the rest of the dishes had been washed, dried and packed away already. And then it would be time to go home.

Some days, if he can manage it, we drive with my father through the green, oak-lined Constantia winelands, over the mountain and into the valley below, following a winding road that goes all the way to the sea at Hout Bay. We bring my father here for the drive, the view, but mostly for the gelato. In the corner of a parking lot, its bricks raised by the roots of milkwood trees, is a small ice-cream shop run by an Italian family. So small that there is barely enough room for four people to stand side by side in it. Here they make gelato in the traditional Italian way, without preservatives or colourants. The shop is owned by an Italian brother and sister; the brother also runs the neighbouring Italian restaurant where he does the cooking himself in full view of the customers, singing all the while and shouting at his staff. Outside, at picnic tables, we sit and wait as my father slowly works his way through a single scoop. If he is tired or cold we sit in the car, watching the milkwood trees move in the breeze. On the drive back we will be quiet, passing the informal settlement without comment. We will ignore the small cemetery to our right that children sometimes play in. My father will doze, and when we arrive home he will go to bed, sleeping for hours.

One evening while we are watching *Carry on Camping*, my father asks for some ice-cream. When I go to the freezer, there is only chocolate, a flavour he has never liked. I place a small scoop in a bowl for him. In another I pile the ice-cream high. I have never liked chocolate ice-cream either, but as my father eats less and less I find myself eating more and more. I gain weight rapidly, becoming larger as he shrinks. I hand the small bowl over to him, apologising that it is chocolate-flavoured. He smiles and says it doesn't matter as he cannot taste anyway. It is only the texture he likes, soft and cool on his swollen tongue. The sensation is familiar to me and I remind him of my failed trip to Italy when I was 18 years old. How I developed chickenpox the day I arrived. How the spots spread across my body, sitting on my eyelids, eardrums, inside my nostrils. How my mouth was swollen with blisters. In Pisa, Venice, Rome I was able to eat nothing but gelato. On a square in Florence I ordered soup, exorbitantly priced, sitting as we were in the shadows of ancient statues. It was served in the traditional fashion with bread crumbled into the bowl. Despite being softened by the soup, in my swollen mouth the bread was as rough as gravel. This is amongst my limited memories of Italy. The illness knocked me out. I spent most of the time asleep in my tent in various campsites across the country. In Rome I was so ill that I was placed in a wooden cabin free of charge. For two days I did not leave the cabin, peeing in a wastepaper bin without shame.

I would have told my father all of this before, but he seems to be enjoying listening to me, so I tell him again of how in Florence we asked for a doctor to be called. He came, up a tree-lined hill on a small white scooter, his long legs sticking out awkwardly. Tears ran down his cheeks and he moaned from time to time as he examined me. An interpreter explained that the doctor's fiancée was in New York and that the twin towers had just been bombed a few hours earlier. It was September 11th 2001. The doctor had no idea whether his fiancée was alive or dead. Months later, back in South Africa, I looked for a list of those killed in the terrorist attack, searching for Italian names. There were several, but I could not be certain that any of them were the doctor's fiancée. I had no proof that she was Italian anyway, no idea of who or what she was.

When I return to my travel diary of the time, there are no entries about my stay in Italy apart from a scrawled announcement that I have chickenpox and a short note to my father, written while I was in Rome in the wooden cabin.

Daddy
I am in Rome and have seen nothing. All my life this has been my dream and here I am with nothing. When I come home we can go to the pub and talk about Europe. You can tell me about Italy. I have missed it all.

How silly this seems now, the daydream of an 18-year-old girl, fresh from her independence in England, believing she will frequent pubs with her father on her return home – a man who had

133

never given any sign of being interested in going to a pub. It was a foolish thought, and of course we did not ever go. But on that night, sitting on my parents' bed, he tells me to pause the movie which we have long since stopped watching and bring him his Italy photo album.

He and my mother went together on a tour organised by the South African Onderwys Unie (Teachers Union) in the early 1970s. The chaperone was an elderly man who took all the young males aside before the trip, warning them that Europe was a hotbed of sin and vices. They were to be vigilant, keeping their eyes peeled and staying true to their Christian upbringings. South Africa, deep in its apartheid years, was a censor's dream. Very little was left unbanned and the chaperone cautioned the men to carry those bans with them in their hearts. There would be no purchasing of *Playboy*, no photos of naked statues, no strolls through the red-light districts. Most specifically, they were not to meddle with any of the women on the tour. He gave my father, who had been seeing my mother for a year or more, a warning glare. 'There will be no funny business,' he said in Afrikaans. 'Just because you're English-speaking doesn't mean you can forget you are South African and a gentleman.'

Once in Italy, my father shunned the chaperone, taking my mother on his own tour, showing her the sites that he wanted to see and relating the histories of these places with great detail and a characteristic flourish of his hands. They walked for hours each day, folding and unfolding a map and referring to a small notebook that my father carried in the breast pocket of his shirt.

My father talks me through the unlabelled photos in the album; they are not organised by region or city, yet he knows where each snapshot was taken and what else occurred around that moment. The photos themselves are fairly obscure. An insignificant alleyway, a market seen from above, a rock face, a small harbour, the plaster cast of a person dying in agony at Pompeii, a curio stall at Pisa, the nativity at the Baptistery of St John, the Fontana dei Quattro Fiumi in Piazza Navona which features the Obelisk of Domitian and where he and my mother took off their shoes and cooled their hot feet in the water before being chased away by *polizia*.

Finally, on the last page, a lake photographed from a mountain road above. It flows outwards, past mountains, through to the sea. It is Lake Garda, the largest lake in Italy, stretching from the high Alps to the warm plains of Lombardy, narrowing as it extends so that it has what some refer to as a phallic silhouette. Perhaps the shape is apt considering what I know of one of the villas that sits on its shores in the town of Gardone Riviera.

'When you were in Lombardy, did you go to D'Annunzio's villa?' I ask my father. 'It's called Il Vittoriale Degli Italiani – the Victory Monument of the Italians.'

'I don't know,' he says. 'I don't think so.'

'You would remember it,' I say, though I know of the villa through books only. 'It was the retirement home of Gabriele D'Annunzio and is now open to the public as a museum. He is one of my favourite authors, haven't you ever heard of him?'

'No,' he replies and I begin to tell him about this strange man whose talents were vast, his peculiarities many.

Il Vittoriale was a home that D'Annunzio bought with a bank loan that he never paid back. Fond of excess, the man lived in extremes of wealth and poverty, spending money he did not have. Eventually, compelled by the great plans he had for renovating the villa, he deeded the land and its contents to the nation on the condition that Italy pay for his redevelopment schemes. Surprisingly the proposal was agreed to and D'Annunzio was able to go ahead and build the Priory, which comprised the main building of the estate. The Priory, perhaps, is nothing more than a monument to the man himself, though he insisted it was a nod to the ascetic lives of monks whom he admired very much. Yet, this same man ordered his servants to toll the bells announcing to the estate and community at large each time he achieved orgasm.

The bedroom, known as the Leper Room, features a bed made to resemble at once a crib and a coffin, representing the link between life and death. Beside the bed a painting depicts D'Annunzio as a leper being nursed by St Francis of Assisi, while in a fresco on the ceiling are painted female saints bearing the faces of his many lovers. His study is preceded by three steps and a low ceiling, forcing the entrant to bow as they enter. It is said that D'Annunzio, though short, frequently banged his head on the low lintel. The man cared greatly for clothing and in his drawers can still be found 73 pairs of monogrammed silk underwear, 300 pairs of boots and shoes designed by himself, a nightshirt with a gold-embroidered hole for love-making, full-sized baby outfits for his mistresses, and boxes containing tufts of his lovers' pubic hair. The estate holds, too, a mausoleum, statues of his greyhounds, the light cruiser *Puglia* embedded in a hillside, and a room of relics from numerous religions.

On the evening of 1 March 1938, 11 days before his 75th birthday, D'Annunzio died in his study while standing in front of his writing lectern. Suicide by means of overdose has been suggested. By then he considered himself to be nothing more than a 'shitting biped' and seems to have lost interest in living.

Born in 1863, D'Annunzio found little value in tradition and lived by a credo entirely his own, a credo dominated by sensuality and absurd fascinations. In his teenage years he pawned his grandfather's pocket watch to fund a visit to a brothel and sent out press releases announcing his death in order to win publicity for his first volume of poetry, *Primo Vere*. He wrote widely: essays, poetry, short stories, plays, novels, in a style both new and shocking with its focus on the subtleties of sensation, the joys of voluptuousness. His first novel, *Il Piacere* (Pleasure), is semi-autobiographical, featuring a protagonist who seeks to enjoy 'horrible sacrileges' and 'experiences never tried'.

A decidedly unattractive man, D'Annunzio was bald by his early twenties, had rotten teeth, spindly legs, was blind in one eye – eyes that Sarah Bernhardt described as being like blobs of shit – and was coarse in manner. Yet women flocked to him, allowing him the opportunity to move from affair to affair. He boasted of his lovers exceeding a thousand, despite a 55-year marriage to Duchess Maria Harduin. His lovers include the actress Eleanora Duse, whose spirit he communicated with after her death by biting into a pomegranate and standing in front of a statue of Buddha. Another lover, Luisa Casati, wore live snakes as necklaces and kept black male servants whom she painted gold.

D'Annunzio's social and political beliefs were Nietzschean and he wrote that 'Men will be divided into two races. To the superior race, which shall have risen by the pure energy of its will, all shall be permitted; to the lower, nothing or very little.' This belief was coupled with fierce political ideas that secured his popularity in the day and fed into later fascism. He was a rabid nationalist who campaigned for Italy to enter the First World War. He served in the army, navy and air corps, and lost the sight in one eye during a plane crash. After 18 August 1918, he was considered a hero for leading eight planes over Vienna, scattering 50,000 leaflets addressed to the Viennese. The text was penned by him, and audaciously not translated into German:

On this August morning, while the fourth year of your desperate convulsion comes to an end and luminously begins the year of our full power, suddenly there appears the three-colour wing as an indication of the destiny that is turning.

D'Annunzio's enthusiastic jingoism won him many followers after the war, especially when he spoke of a united Italy and championed the idea of national pride. He raised an army of men he called his *arditi* (the daring ones) who numbered in the region of two and a half thousand and wore a uniform of black shirts. Together they seized Fiume, a city with a majority Italian population, which the Paris Peace Conference had given to Yugoslavia. To the embarrassment of the Italian government, several ships mutinied and offered their service to D'Annunzio. Little more was done and the man was able to rule his small republic for nearly two years without hindrance.

He announced himself to be Duce of the port town, changing its name to Carnaro and drawing up a constitution that, alongside anarchic and proto-fascist ideas, declared music one of the fundamental principles of the Fiume State. Article 65 of the constitution reads:

> In every commune of the province there will be a choral
> society and an orchestra subsidised by the State. In
> the city of Fiume, the College of Aediles [magistrates]
> will be commissioned to erect a great concert hall,
> accommodating an audience of at least ten thousand with
> tiers of seats and ample space for choir and orchestra. The
> great orchestral and choral celebrations will be entirely
> free, in the language of the Church, a gift of God.

It is to his credit that D'Annunzio really did institute free concerts for his citizens. Every morning he read poetry and manifestos from his balcony; every evening there was a concert, then fireworks. Eventually this idyll ended when the Italian navy bombarded the city in 1921. Defeated, D'Annunzio moved back to Italy and retired to his beloved villa. In the mausoleum he laid to rest those of his *arditi* who had died in defending their republic.

By now my father's ice-cream is melted in the bowl, unfinished. He is fascinated by D'Annunzio and says he wishes he had heard about him sooner. There is no time now for him to read about D'Annunzio and his relationship with Mussolini, who modelled much of his own behaviour on that of the poet and who always felt somewhat threatened by him.

Dictators intrigue my father. His bookcase is heavy with biographies of Lenin, Stalin, Hitler, Mao Tse Tung, Mussolini. To me, my father's interest in such people has always seemed sourceless. Yet as we sit, the Italy album before us, my father begins to tell me about his Uncle Albert, a man who wore the bonnet of fascism until it crushed him. Perhaps watching a man's life deteriorating in that fashion sparked some need in my father to read about these leaders, investigating what drove and destroyed them.

Albert Carr was the husband of my grandmother's sister, Peggy. He had moved to South Africa from England after the First World War with his parents and his brother, Douglas. When the Second World War broke out, the brothers fought with the South African forces. What happened during that time of unrest is beyond memory now and cannot be explained, but somehow war turned both men into rabid fascists. On returning home, Albert and Douglas immediately rejected their British ancestry and joined every right-wing organisation that they could find. Somewhere on the battlefields a seed had been planted in them that grew into the belief that the Afrikaans people were God's chosen race. It was their responsibility to uphold Germanic civilisation at all costs. Both brothers campaigned hard in the 1948 election and eventually Douglas became a National Party senator in the 1960s.

Albert, the younger of the two, was an even more avid fascist. Every aspect of his life was governed by rules of his own making, rules that would ensure he lived in an idyllic state, free from Jews and coloured or black people. Because of Louis (who was Jewish) being on the guest list, he did not go to my grandparents' wedding. He refused to allow Peggy to be a bridesmaid at the same wedding, as he claimed it would 'perpetuate British Imperialism', though what he meant by this no one knew. He reduced both his and Peggy's lives to a small circle of acceptable people and activities. She was not allowed to buy the monthly groceries from OK Bazaars as it was owned by Jews. Instead she had to buy them far more expensively at the local shop on the corner, which was run and owned by an Afrikaner. This was easy enough for him to demand, as it was Peggy who bore the financial burden of their household. Unable to keep any job because he was being 'victimised by the Jews who were watching' him, Albert spent his days on a large plot of land where he kept poultry. They were his only friends, he said, and he never killed a single one. He had seen too much violence during the war, he would tell people quietly.

One Saturday, visiting the Carrs with his parents, my father, who was a second-year university student at the time, came across Albert in the garden with chickens sitting on his lap. Albert looked at my father and asked what subjects he was studying at university. 'History,' my father replied, and Albert asked if they had studied the Second World War. 'Not yet,' he said. My father told me, as though it were happening before his eyes, that Albert turned away from him, stroking the back of a chicken, which clucked as the man spoke: 'He was right. Hitler. Just think what it would be like now if he had got rid of all the Jews. This would be a wonderful world.'

I have already decided that my birthday will be spent in much the same way as I would spend any other day. I tend to the flowers on our small balcony, clean the bathroom and do some haphazard spring-cleaning before I have to leave for my marking job in the late afternoon. A drawer that has been sticking for months is over-full with old notebooks. I reorganise them, but one large one, an A4 exercise book, won't fit no matter which way I try to angle it. I consider throwing it away, thinking it is only a notebook, but when I open it I find that it is a journal, kept in the latter half of my second year at university.

My undergraduate years were a difficult time. I had been in and out of the clinic a few times and struggled with being an adult under my parents' roof. For most of my teenage years and all the way through my early twenties my father and I clashed. We are both rash, prone to pettiness, find it difficult to admit when we are wrong. My father was, in my mind, a dictator, squashing the life out of me. In the journal I find this diagram and description of life with him at the time:

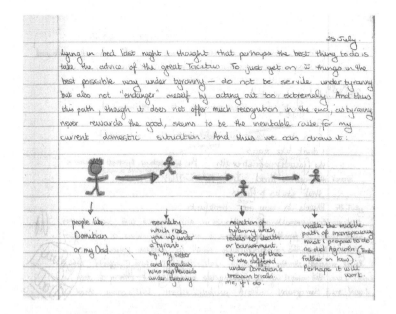

Lying in bed last night I thought that perhaps the best thing to do is take the advice of the great Tacitus. To just get on w̄ things in the best possible way under tyranny — do not be servile under tyranny but also not "endanger" oneself by acting out too extremely. And thus this path, though it does not offer much recognition in the end, as tyranny never rewards the good, seems to be the inevitable route for my current domestic situation. And thus we can draw it:

people like Domitian or my Dad.

servility which raises you up under a tyrant. eg. my sister and Regulus who reap rewards under tyranny.

rejection of tyranny which leads to death or banishment. eg. many of those who suffered under Domitian's treason trials. me, if I do.

walk the middle path of inconspicuous what I propose to do as did Agricola (Tacitus father in law). Perhaps it will work.

I am surprised when I read this. By now all recollection of my father as being a tyrant is gone. Yet, when I think about it, certain memories arise. One is of a man who terrified me. I was perhaps six years old and my mother was sick in bed with flu. My father, as he often did on weekend nights, watched a film musical with my sister and I. This time it was *Chitty Chitty Bang Bang*. I sat on his lap throughout, frightened by the Child Catcher with his long nose that smells out children. Once I had been put to bed, the Child Catcher stayed with me, my night-light making his shadow appear on every wall and corner. I began to scream for my mother, loudly, continuously. Then a featureless body appeared in my bedroom doorway and I heard my father's voice, 'Your mother isn't coming. Do you hear me? She isn't coming anymore, so you can keep screaming, but she won't come.'

But that is not the behaviour of a tyrant, surely? A man who was tired of a daughter who, in fact, screamed every night and only slept through when she was four years old. A man who wanted his daughter, who invented fears with or without movies, to become independent is not the act of a dictator, yet the memory to this day is violent in my mind.

There must be other incidents. There must be an event, a disagreement, something that I can put my finger on and say, yes, this is why I hated my father for so long. But there is nothing solid, just a weak memory of a fight with my father when I was 24. The content of the argument I cannot recall, only his words: 'I can stop loving you like that!' He snapped his fingers. 'It will be like I never even knew you.' And my response, predictable, 'I hate you so much.' Days later there was an apology, wordless, as he took me out for a meal at my favourite restaurant. We sat awkwardly, both of us relieved that the neighbouring shop was undergoing renovations. Above the hammering and other sounds there was no possibility of hearing, and therefore no need to speak.

What I do know is that I can mark my removal of myself from the family at the time when I drew the diagram. I withdrew myself, barely spoke to my father. Tried to be at home as little as possible, or if I was at home I would be alone in my room. If he spoke, I flinched. If he came near me I turned away. I am ashamed to remember it now, though such behaviour is not unusual in young people trying to assert their own personhood.

I look at the diagram again. By now I have forgotten my undergraduate studies. I do not remember the significance of Domitian, nor of Agricola and Regulus, so I go to my bookshelf and find my copy of Suetonius' *Twelve Caesars* – in fact, it is my father's copy with a moth-eaten cover and his name scrawled on the inside page, my name below it. We both used this book to study from. I had turned to Classics in my second year, shunning English, barely going to lectures. Perhaps the reason for this behaviour is complicated, yet perhaps it is as simple as this: my father was an English teacher. English was his subject and I wanted to rip him out of myself.

The names in the *Twelve Caesars* don't matter, nor who they are or what they did. I read the pages blindly, able only to think that this emperor who had people killed, who was paranoid, cruel and spiteful, is nothing like my father. I look again at my journal and see an entry dated a bit more than a month after the previous one:

> So much changes without changing. I found a letter on my bed today. It is from my dad. He writes of the pain he feels about the pain I feel. How he misses knowing me. Misses seeing me smile and talk. When he comes home and sees my bedroom door closed he hates it. He has promised to make more of an effort. He will relent, I hope, some of his dictatorial qualities. It seems that everything is standing still... I feel terrible for my dad. He is a stranger already. Perhaps I will try. But it is hard.

These are things we have to face, those of us who have lost a parent. Memories, shameful, in which each of us, parent and child, is a person unrecognisable with distance. Yet it is a person that we feel responsible for nonetheless, and it is their guilt that we carry with us like a scar from a forgotten injury.

PART SIX: TRAVELLING WITH THE DEAD

This is our second Christmas without my father. Last year I was away in India on a three-month residency; I was phoned by my mother mid-morning to be told that my Ouma had passed away a few hours before. This year Juliano's sister and teenage cousin have come from São Paulo to spend Christmas and New Year with us. We take them to the usual tourist attractions – Boulders, Hout Bay, Chapman's Peak, and Cape Point which they have learnt about at school through Camões and his epic *Os Lusíados*. Juliano waits in the car park while Janaina, Mayara and I climb the steep path up to the top of the Point. 'There,' I say, indicating a rough patch of white where waves are breaking in an otherwise still sea. 'That is where the two oceans meet.' It is what my father told me when I was young and, even though there is no truth to it, I have pointed it out each time I have been to Cape Point since.

I am proud to show Juliano's family around Cape Town, though I am careful to mention that the city is more than just its beautiful mountains, winelands and beaches. It has a difficult history, as does the rest of the country. While we drive around the peninsula I tell them as much as I can about the past of the city, of the cultures that met here. I am aware that I am droning. Mayara is playing on her phone, Janaina's eyes glaze over. Still, I keep talking; it is myself that I am telling.

Cape Town emerges out of the slopes of Table Mountain in a strangely layered way. Layers that testify to racialist urban planning under the apartheid regime. The first layer belongs to the privileged, predominantly white inhabitants and spreads through the city centre and the nearby suburbs. Beyond lie the Cape Flats: suburbs and suburbs of working-class coloured families, many of whom were forcibly removed in the 1960s from desirable locations in the city centre. Considered by the government as a 'coloured labour preference area', Cape Town city planners kept these labourers near at hand, but far enough that they need not see them after the end of the working day. The Cape Flats is now a hotbed of drugs and gangster-ism. Beyond the Cape Flats is the third layer: the vast informal settlements comprising largely Xhosa-speakers, but home, too, to many refugees from various war-torn African neighbours. These are the places that we do not show our guests, not beyond pointing in their direction from the highway.

Most of the year this general segregation continues, but something happens in and around 15 December of every year that changes everything. Traditionally, this is the last day of work for many blue-collar businesses: builders, labourers, contract-workers, artisans of every sort. As soon as the clock strikes 5pm on 15 December, Cape Town undergoes at once a mass exodus and a mass influx. A movement of bodies and cars and trains and buses that does not cease until the New Year. The exodus occurs in the townships on a magnificent scale. The Transkei and Ciskei regions of the Eastern Cape remain the Xhosa heartland; poor areas that send their sons and daughters to other provinces in order to have a better life. At Christmas those that can afford to return to the Eastern Cape to join their families. It is a festive, but dangerous, time. South Africa's roads are full of heavily laden cars, over-crowded buses and minibuses. The death toll is always high. In the evenings we hear the increasing number of the dead announced on the news.

As for the influx, this occurs predominantly from the Cape Flats into the city bowl. By this stage the switching on of the Christmas lights in Adderley Street has already occurred, and each night the road is closed to traffic, making way for a night market. It is a strange sort of Christmas market, for the stall-holders are largely Muslim, selling the traditional food of the Cape Town Muslim: *gatsbies* and *koeksisters* and samoosas. Muslims also make up the crowd of revellers, as foreign as tourists in many ways. Whole families with granny and grandpa and baby and aunty descend on the city centre, their wallets bursting with Christmas bonuses. All the children run around looking at the lights, eating themselves sick, going mad with the joy of it all. The old people bring their own chairs. They sit in the middle of the fairway and talk to passers-by, loudly. At the end of the street, towards the Golden Acre Mall, a temporary stage is set up. Unknown pop groups perform here. Stand-up comedians make jokes so coded in Cape Coloured culture that even I, who have lived in Cape Town for all of my life, do not understand them. There is no need to wonder at the presence of all these people. The desire to enjoy oneself, to relax after a year of hard work, is a secular one. One motivated too for these people from the Flats by a year-round life of unsafe neighbourhoods, gunshots at night, worry and hardship. Under the Christmas lights in Adderley Street they can forget the dangers of ordinary days.

'It's different,' Janaina tells me. 'Very different to Christmas in Brazil.' But she doesn't elaborate, and I don't press her. We cannot hear one another above the sound of the pop group and the Christmas revellers around us.

Last year was my first Christmas away from South Africa, and the first not spent in the big house. Of course, Christmastime is usually burdened with nostalgia of every sort, and I found myself, in a rural village in south India, facing that nostalgia more and more as the holiday approached. I spent the day in the sultry heat of an Indian winter, eating vegetarian curry, chapattis and curd, followed by for dessert. My Ouma would not wake me at 5am from my makeshift bed on the couch to ask me (still, after more than 30 years) where my mother keeps the sugar. My father would not set the dining room table while singing Welsh choral favourites. I would not taste my grandmother's famous trifle.

This year I am separated from these things too, not by distance, but by loss. The big house is gone, my grandmother, father and Ouma are dead. My grandmother's trifle recipe went with her to the grave.

These are the things that come to us when we are removed from those we love, be it by distance or by death. The rituals of lives shared, brought together.

I am going through a cupboard in my office at my mother's house in preparation for my next trip to India when I find items that I had stowed away months before during my mother's move; items that I had not bothered to look at before. A box of theatre programmes, perhaps 100 of them, or more. Shows my father had seen in Cape Town, overseas, through all the years of his life. Some of them are duplicates – ballets or operettas that he went to each year that they were being performed. There are programmes too from the school plays he directed, and from concerts that my sister and I performed in. What does one do with these? Hundreds of glossy pages that he took so much care in keeping. Of what value are they to any of us now?

Behind the box is a metre-long stick upon which is rolled a wide strip of paper as long as a man. In a meticulous and tiny hand the family trees of all the royal houses of Europe have been drawn. In the corner are my father's name and the year, 1966. He was 20 years old, spending his evenings mapping out bloodlines with such care. I have no interest in the scroll. What would be lost if I were to throw it away?

Finally, there is a blue notebook which I have never seen before. Inside are newspaper articles about Halley's Comet that my father pasted into the book in February, March and April of 1986. On a blank page dated 12 April 1986, with the time noted as 19:56, he recorded my response to the event: 'I saw Harry's comet, but I didn't see it.' I was three and a half years old. And yet, despite my age, I remember that night. My father taking us out into the dark, the excitement of being about to see this thing that he had spoken of for days. I know that I saw nothing despite my father's pointing. I know because it was something I felt ashamed of, not having been able to see it. But now, reading the newspaper clippings, I see that visibility was poor that night, and not many witnessed the comet in Cape Town.

Eventually, no doubt, I will throw this notebook away, but for the moment I page through it. One of the clippings is folded over, too large to fit on the page. On the back is a photograph of a girl and a notice announcing that she is missing. I recognise her. Not because I ever knew her, but because her face has etched itself into my childhood. Not hers alone; there are faces of several girls, all white. We saw them on posters, in *You* magazine and *Huisgenoot*. For years the same six or seven girls, none of them ever found.

It was a troubled time in South Africa; a state of emergency, the collapse of apartheid, the threats, ever-present, of violence. At school we were regularly rehearsed in bomb-threat procedure, in how to hide under our desks. Police spoke to us in the school hall with plastic replicas of weapons and drugs; everywhere there was danger – no one could be trusted.

I may have been eight years old when I located a white scar high up on my forehead. Small, already covered in freckles. It was enough though to send me to my parents, wailing.

'I know the truth,' I said. 'I know what you did.'

'What are you talking about?' my mother asked.

'You kidnapped me and operated on my brain and put memories in it so that I would think you are my parents.'

There was nothing they could say to still my crying. Not even the photograph album with the sonogram showing me in the womb alongside the twin who had died two months before birth. Not the photos of my parents holding me, carrying me, feeding me.

'How do I know you didn't make these photos to trick me?' I said.

'Oh my girl,' my dad sighed, 'why do you always have to make things so difficult?'

'I don't know.'

By now I was less convinced of my kidnapping and brainwashing, but not certain. I held onto my father, crying into his armpit. Even if he wasn't my father, I liked the way he smelled.

Since meeting, Juliano and I have said goodbye to one another at airports too many times to count on both hands. We seem always to be in separate countries, never together for longer than two months at a time. Less than four months after we began our relationship, I went to India for three months. The time apart was challenging. We argued and felt uncertain. We barely knew one another. Now, more than a year later I am leaving for India again, this time for seven weeks. Juliano's contract in South Africa ends while I am away. A week after I return he goes to Harvard for a three-month fellowship. After that, we do not know. He may have to return to Brazil, or stay in America, or perhaps, if we are lucky, he will find work in South Africa. Nothing is certain and it is difficult for us to feel confident in a future that has no place as yet.

As the second anniversary of my father's death approaches, my sister suggests that it might be a good time for us to scatter his ashes. I am surprised by the suddenness of the decision. I am not sure how ready I am for this moment. My mother and I are driving together into Town to organise my visa for India when she tells me that she doesn't want to part with the ashes – she is still using them. I ask her what she means. She explains that she has taken to scattering small amounts of his ashes in places that she comes to. The first was in Udaipur on the anniversary of his death. She had joined me in India and we had toured Rajasthan together for three weeks. We were never apart during that time. When did she have a chance to throw my father's ashes in Pichola Lake? Why only tell me now?

Other places hold my father's ashes, she reveals to me now. The corner of the garden of the big house, a patch of Golden Gate. Later in the year she has a trip to Croatia planned with her cousins. He will accompany her there too. She asks whether I think her behaviour strange. 'No,' I tell her. 'We are both travelling with him in our own way.'

My mother twists her rings nervously and is reminded of something that happened a few days before. She tells me the story in laborious detail that only my mother can master. She bumped into a former neighbour whose husband died six months after my father. The woman is surprised to see my mother wearing her wedding rings and explains that she took hers off as soon as her husband died. 'I am not married anymore,' the woman says. Apart from her engagement ring, my mother has three slim wedding bands, representing each of the three decades that she and my father were married. One of them was melted down and created from a wedding band that had to be sawn off Uncle Vic's finger after his death. I remember my grandmother telling me of her own mother's fingers swelling in the months preceding her death. Her ring too had to be removed with violence, decades after her husband's death.

Days later my mother, sister and I visit the botanical gardens at Kirstenbosch on the anniversary of my father's death. We go to the place where my grandmother's ashes were scattered and where he wished to be scattered too. The view is beautiful: a green hill surrounded by plants and trees, the city in the distance and, further still, mountains. But the path that has been built over the area since my grandmother's scattering means the spot is busier than we would like it to be. We sit for a long time, the three of us, talking about where Juliano and I might move to and when, watching as couples and tourists pass us.

At a still moment my mother brings out a small plastic box. Inside are some of my dad's ashes, less than a handful. 'Is anyone around?' she asks. 'I want to throw your father away quickly.' We laugh at this. There is no ceremony to the moment. Only my sister and I on the bench as my mother tosses ash into a bed of shrubs as easily as one might toss out the dregs of a teacup. It is not the moment that I had anticipated and I am glad for that. There is no sadness, no sense of loss. We are a family together, laughing.

I arrive in India two days before my residency at Nrityagram dance village begins. I have never been to India before and don't know what to expect, my only engagement with the country, my only interest in fact, having been through E.M. Forster's *A Passage to India*. For years this novel has existed amongst my favourites and is home to what I consider the best sentence in English fiction: 'League after league the earth lies flat, heaves a little, is flat again.' So it is this that I anticipate finding in India; flat land, not much more. But it is not what I encounter at all.

For two nights I will stay in Cooke Town, an ex-colonial area that is now a suburb of the vast city of Bengaluru (Bangalore). The drive from the airport takes an hour and a half. I have arrived in the country late at night, yet the streets are busy, the traffic loud, ever-present. Even in the little residential street where my homestay is, the traffic does not once stop. All night cars, scooters, bicycles ring their bells, honk their horns. No one sleeps here. Not even the dogs, which walk the streets day and night, searching for food. 'India!' I text Juliano during the taxi ride. 'There is no escaping it. Once you are in India you are in INDIA.'

Hours of travel have left me exhausted and so I am more than a little dismayed when I see my room at the homestay. The bed is sheetless, the pillow fetid, stained. I have only an old, scratchy blanket with holes in it to cover myself with. The en-suite bathroom is massive, larger than the room itself, tiled in green, with no separate shower, only a showerhead that sticks out of the wall above the toilet so that I have to straddle the toilet bowl in order to get my body wet. I sleep on my damp towel, a jumper as a pillow, a scarf as a blanket. It is not more than a doze though. The noise of the street keeps me awake, and by dawn I dress myself and decide to go for a walk outside. The hallway is dark and before I reach the front door, I trip over a 'boy' who is asleep on the floor, wrapped in another scratchy blanket.

In the street there is a faint mist, though the weather is mild. It is November, the heart of winter, and everywhere I look people are dressed for the season. Children, barely clothed, wear monkey-topis (balaclavas), while men in little more than lungis and shirts wear earmuffs. It is a general south Indian belief that if your ears are covered then you are protected from all ailments, including the cold. Even the dogs are dressed for winter, wearing jackets and sometimes human jerseys. People are kind; they do not forget the strays and dress them too.

I walk to a park nearby that is bordered on two sides by blocks of flats. The park has a circuit along which various people are walking. Old men in tracksuit pants and T-shirts, young men in designer training gear, women in saris with running shoes sticking out below. All of them walking with concentration. After a few laps the men stand in the centre of the park and do exercises that look like they come from a 1950s physical education handbook. I join the route, jogging slowly around and around the park.

Sounds coming from the open windows of the flats in the neighbouring blocks remind me of home. When I first moved in with Juliano, I was woken every morning at around 6am by the sound of one of our neighbours retching. I had seen them on their balcony a few times and knew that they were Indian. The woman wore saris and spoke no English. Her husband went to work dressed in a suit and tie. 'She must be pregnant,' I said to Juliano, thinking the noise was morning sickness, but he told me that for the past year and a half he had been woken by that sound. 'One of them is very sick, but it's not pregnancy,' he said. Now as I jog the endless circuit of the small park, that retching sound comes to me, not once, but a dozen times over, echoing out from various open windows. A dozen lungs being cleared in preparation for the day.

Two days later I leave Cooke Town for the countryside and Nrityagram. Nrityagram is a *gurukal* or residential school that takes the form of a dance village. It was founded in 1990 by

155

Protima Gauri who described it as 'a community of dancers in a forsaken place amidst nature. A place where nothing exists, except dance. A place where you breathe, eat, sleep, dream, talk, imagine – dance. A place where all the five senses can be refined to perfection.'

I am not a dancer, of course, but for several months every year Nrityagram plays host to visiting writers. We dine with the dancers daily, eating vegetarian meals prepared from food grown on the grounds, and we are invited to watch their rehearsals. The principal dance studied at Nrityagram is Odissi, one of the eight classical dance forms of India. Most of the techniques and moves were lost over time as it was suppressed under British colonial rule. However, in recent decades Odissi has been resurrected through careful study of reliefs and statues in ancient temples. There is nothing easy about the dance form, and at Nrityagram they spend hours each day practising in the heat, until the floor beneath them is slick with sweat. In the three months that I am there, I cannot persuade myself to watch rehearsals above a few times. Their commitment frightens me, makes me feel guilty about the empty pages in my notebook and the hours spent walking on the plain or playing with the three Nrityagram dogs.

I am too much in love with my surroundings to spend very long at my desk. The grounds of Nrityagram are lush, inhabited by birds and insects and small squirrels with a stripe down their back. Every second morning I run 6 kilometres to the nearest village, Hesaraghatta, and then back again. I pass the strange and vast government poultry breeding farms, where different gates advertise Turkey Unit, Ostrich Unit, Chicken Unit, Duck Unit, Emu Unit. It is early in the morning and I see people coming from the foliage beside the road where they have been defecating, or men on bicycles laden with pots of water that they have filled at the standpipe.

A few weeks after my arrival there is a dreadful and highly publicised rape case in Delhi where a 23-year-old woman was gang raped by six men who had lured her into a private bus.

She later died of the injuries sustained. We have been speaking about this a lot, the writers, and each day the papers have stories about new rapes or reveal the amount of rapes that occur in the countryside. I read that fathers of rape victims in rural areas regularly drink poison in order to escape the shame of a soiled daughter. This is on my mind as I run one morning while it is still dark in order to avoid the heat of the day. I begin to hear soft footfalls on the dirt road behind me. I become increasingly unsettled as they grow faster and faster. I am being approached. I prepare myself for an attack and turn around suddenly, flashing the small torch that I carry with me. The beam lands on the face of a goat that bleats at me, before turning away and trotting towards a patch of grass on the side of the road.

Why this goat was alone and why it was chasing me, I don't know, though it is not unusual to see goats or cattle on the road early in the morning. There is a large grass plain next to Nrityagram where herders take their animals to graze. Often the plain is used as a film set and then hordes of costumed people march up and down it for a few days at a time filming historical dramas or battles between gods and goddesses. In the background the herders watch with mild curiosity, the cattle oblivious. Stray dogs approach, looking for food.

When I leave Nrityagram to meet my mother in Delhi, I am leaving behind the best place I have ever known. Delhi, on the other hand, is rabid. Everywhere you look there is a battle occurring. People squabble for room on a pavement. Tuk-tuk drivers are at war with one another. Cars jostle. Delhi chews me up, spits me out. After the countryside, I am unprepared for being pursued, befriended, cajoled, over-charged, tricked, insulted, charmed with every step. I am unprepared too for my mother, who is thinner, older, weaker. In the three months since I have seen her, her mother has died, and she has been alone in a big house that is falling apart. She has been grieving. But the effect that the traffic, the noise, the colour, the punters and tricksters has on her is surprising. Everything excites her and she throws herself into India head first, unafraid.

For three weeks we travel together, mostly through Rajasthan in the northern part of India. Much of the time we cover distances by train. The great Indian railway system is amongst the world's largest railway networks. With 115,000 kilometres of track over 65,000 kilometres of land, it serves 24 million passengers daily. There is a variety of types of trains and carriages, with eight different levels of comfort and class, and we experience most of them. Short trips through Delhi's sprawling metropolis by underground metro; two-hour journeys in un-air-conditioned second class where the floors are covered in peanut shells; executive air-conditioned long-distance journeys where food is constantly being brought to us along with endless servings of sweet tea; and finally, an all-night three-tier sleeper train which is stuffy, smelling of spices and flatulence. Sometimes, as we emerge from these trains onto the platforms, my mother and I are separated by the current of movement that flows simultaneously towards the train and away from it. There is no way of stopping, once you are in a tide you can only move along with it. Fortunately, in comparison with most Indians, we are both tall and fair and so we are able to keep one another's bobbing heads in view as best we can.

Before she came to India, I asked my mother to bring along a notebook she found amongst my father's things while I was away. On the opening page he wrote the dates of each of the years of his life until the age of 23. Next to the year he wrote the place where he lived and the school or university he attended. After that follow four pages of what he had planned would be Part One of his autobiography. His memories are vivid, but brief. Illness took over before he was able to write anything more. I look at these pages often as my mother and I travel around north India on the various trains. He is always with us. Everywhere we go, everything we eat, see or buy, we wonder whether my father would have liked it. We cannot decide. But the trains, those I know he would have liked, because in the four pages of notes that were to make up his autobiography, my father wrote that his earliest memory was of a train journey.

My first clear memory is of travelling on a train. Sitting on the upper bunk playing with my toys. So I must have been 2 years old and we were on our way to Salisbury in Rhodesia in 1949. [They lived there for one year.]...

I remember travelling, again by train, to the Victoria Falls. Years later my mother reminded me that we had stayed in the Victoria Falls Hotel which had a shuttle service – miniature train carriages on rails – which travelled the shortish distance from the hotel to the first viewing point. These carriages were pushed to and fro by black workers in the employ of the hotel. I do not remember the Falls but I do remember the carriage ride and laughing as the black men sang us down to the viewing point, and later back to the hotel again...

What I don't remember about Salisbury is that my father's parents, Mom and Pop Jennings, visited us. I have photos of their visit taken in parks and other places but have no memory of it. My mother said that the only reason for the visit was that it was free. As he worked for the South African Railways, my grandfather was entitled to a free pass to travel on any SAR train as far as Blantyre in Nyasaland (Malawi). It was during this visit that my mother was 'ticked off' for not caring enough for her house and family. In Rhodesia in those days the houseboys did all the cooking and cleaning and woe betide any newcomers who wanted to rock the boat by not accepting the system. Pop would tell her what he wanted to eat that day, but she informed him that it was her house and she decided on the meals which the houseboy would prepare. This riled him immensely. He was not in control and despised her for it.

My father never spoke about the year that he spent as a toddler in Salisbury, but he did speak of his love of train journeys and many times said that he wanted, above all else, to travel on the Trans-Siberian Railway from Moscow to Vladivostok.

A year after leaving India the first time, I return. This time I stay at Cholamandal artists' village. Despite its name, the village is in fact part of the sprawling metropolis of Chennai and is metres away from a busy main road. The village was founded in 1966 when a number of artists studying at the Madras Government School of Arts and Crafts realised, according to their founder K.C.S. Paniker, that 'since paintings and sculptures do not sell sufficiently, it is necessary to find legitimate means for the serious artist to survive'. The artists came together and bought ten acres of land, which at the time was far outside the city, and began to build houses for themselves. The understanding was that each artist would commit to two hours a day of making craft work such as batiks, enamel jewellery, beaten metalwork and terracotta. These items would be sold and would therefore remove the necessity of artists 'taking up a money-grubbing job'.

Despite by now being surrounded by a sprawling city, Cholamandal still feels like a village with its few quiet dusty streets, forgotten statues and small amphitheatre, leaf-covered, nestled under trees. I stay in a petite apartment above a house that I am told belonged to Arnawaz, one of the original people to live and work at Cholamandal. In 1988 she died at the age of 42 from breast cancer. The property is sandy, lush, bird-rich. Some days, sitting on the balcony I count more than 30 jungle crows in the tree that leans heavily from the sand below up towards the apartment. In the mornings a woman comes to sweep the red earth with a stiff reed broom, leaving swirling patterns behind. By afternoon tamarind and other leaves have fallen; the patterns are gone.

My first week in Chennai I am despondent. I blame it on the relentless heat, the clouds of mosquitoes, jet lag. Any of those might be reason enough, but the truth is that it has been difficult for me to leave home this time. Juliano is depressed. He doesn't talk. He lies on the couch, watches TV. He sleeps, but sleeps poorly. Has nightmares and panic attacks. We are both worried about our future and the fact that there is no certainty. We can make no plans. I am aware that too much of the responsibility lies on his shoulders. He is the breadwinner. As a writer, I have very little to offer that is tangible. The threat of having to take a money-grubbing job is ever present.

On the morning of the first Saturday, I wake early and carefully jog the 250 metres to the beach. In the past few days I have tried going for runs in the area, but it is impossible. There are too many construction sites, cows, goats, cars, bicycles, people. I cannot move without being at risk. In the small fishing village that neighbours Cholamandal, murky water from people's ablutions spreads across the dusty road. People stand in their doorways watching me. Women laugh, children chase me. There are more stray dogs than I can count. They live amongst the garbage on the beach, barking as I pass. The heat is immense, the stench too, and I stop near the water to rest despite the short distance. Nearby a dead dog lies bloating. I turn away. Children are behind me, waving and grinning.

When I return to the grounds of Studio Arnawaz, I find a silver-haired man standing underneath the tamarind tree. I recognise him from a book that I paged through at the small Cholamandal museum and gallery. He is Vasudev, husband of Arnawaz, and works by both of them are on display there. I greet Vasudev, who is kind and polite, but is on his way to a gallery opening and so in a rush. He tells me to visit the Government Museum – paintings of his are there – and mentions that a new 'very thick' book has just been published about him. Then his driver arrives, carefully reversing a large car through the wagon-wheel gate, and, with a wave, Vasudev is gone.

Because I have no other plans for the day, and because I cannot face the relentless heat of the apartment, I organise a taxi to take me to the Museum. In fact, as I find on arrival, the Government Museum is comprised of six separate buildings – Main Building, Front Building, Bronze Gallery, Children's Museum, National Art Gallery and Contemporary Art Gallery – all nestled together on the same grounds. At the time the place speaks to me of nothing more than death and decay. In its gardens are scavenging stray dogs; tired and dirty animal-shaped garbage cans with hollow backs; signs posted at regular intervals declaring that this is a 'litter-free zone', yet the litter is everywhere, even beside the bins, or falling out of holes in their sides.

The museums are not much better. The ground floor in one of the art galleries displays little more than dusty parts of machinery. Upstairs, holograms of rare gold artefacts line the wall. A notice declares that precious items might be stolen and so holograms are the next best thing. They are fuzzy, unclear. It is like looking at an object at the bottom of a dirty pond. Many of them are broken and show only a dark blank. In the Children's Museum costumed dolls depict countries across the globe. Dolls, bald with age, blind, filthy, fallen over in their displays and never picked up. Perhaps the worst is the Museum of Zoology. It is nothing more or less than ancient stuffed animals in various stages of decomposition. A bat has fallen from its perch and has been put back so that it stands on its feet. A display proudly labelled 'Our Ocean World' is manufactured out of a painted papier maché ocean floor upon which stuffed fish lie, having fallen from wires dangling above. Two crabs, their legs long gone, lie like pebbles in the corner.

I am miserable walking alone through all this crumbling mass. Then I hear shrieking, laughter, calls. I am on the mezzanine floor of a gallery lined with displays of rocks and gemstones, and look down. Below me are 100 people, maybe more, and they have surrounded a replica of a tyrannosaurus rex. It is mechanical and moves, gnashing its teeth waving its small front limbs. Roars come from its mouth. We are all entranced. The security guard, who all morning has been blowing his whistle at people with cell phones or cameras, now allows people to video the dinosaur, to have their photos taken beside it. It is a far cry from the dimly-lit, strange proto-dinosaur display at what was the Natural History Museum in Cape Town. My father often took us there when we were children and we would always leave that curious dark corner until last, going first to

162

walk beneath the vast skeleton of a blue whale hanging from the ceiling before sitting in the small yellow booth where whale sounds played. Then came the visitor-empty rooms with their hundreds of stuffed birds and mammals, some of them extinct by now. And in the displays, this I remember clearly, bowls of water, as though left there for the animals to drink.

Perhaps what is most remarkable for me about India is, go to any museum, any gallery or park or palace at any time of the day, any day of the week, and it will be full of visitors. Indians take a great pride in their country, in its history and its objects. In a guide book I read that at any one time in India there are more Indian tourists than foreigners. The packed aisles and halls of the government museum attest to this fact. This is not a museum forgotten, like ones I have visited at home, in Europe, even Australia. Despite the dusty exhibits, these buildings are alive with people. In the grounds children run, men sit in groups, women talk. I have never heard so much noise.

It is dusk by the time I return home. I can hear drums beating, firecrackers exploding. Two nights before I heard similar sounds, following them to the main road where a procession of brightly dressed men and women led a bride and groom in a carriage drawn by ornamented horned cattle. Tonight from my balcony I can see several men carrying a small decorated platform along the dirt road that divides Cholamandal from the construction sites and beach behind. A procession follows, comprised of men alone. They are walking in the direction of the graveyard that is about 200 metres away, where Paniker, the founder of Cholamandal, is buried. Even when they are gone from my view, blocked by trees and distance, I can hear the fireworks, the beating drums and the murmur of conversation.

Two mornings later I walk to the graveyard. A bier decorated with flowers, both real and paper-made, lies at the entrance. Beside it are a plastic bag with empty boxes of sparklers and firecrackers, two small pillows and two shrouds. It is no longer common for the dead to be cremated. The cost is too high, and so in poorer areas such as this, next to the fishing village, burial is increasingly popular. A dog slinks up to me. Her teats are drooping heavily and her flanks are dappled with mange. I have brought some chapattis with me and I toss them to her. She flinches as I throw them, before bolting them down.

She follows me hopefully as I walk amongst the piles of earth that make up the graves. Some of them have been covered in plaster which is now cracking. The sides of one of these piles has been dug away, and a black dog lies sleeping in the hollow. Everywhere there is human excrement, plastic in various forms, glass bottles, cigarette butts. This is where young men come to hang out. I see them in the evenings sometimes, three astride a scooter, making their way to drink and smoke away from their families. An abandoned vendor's trolley is surrounded by broken glass. Men lie on it in the afternoons and doze. The new grave is away from these, on a flat section of sand. Garlands of dying flowers lie on top of the mound. A metallic medallion circles the head of the grave.

Because it is morning, there are men at the standpipe near the entrance to the graveyard. They come here to wash themselves and to collect water to carry home. I never see women and I begin to wonder whether I am trespassing unintentionally. As a result, I begin to time my visits so that I am not present when the men are washing or drinking. However, it is the standpipe, and my ignorance too, that causes me to make a terrible mistake.

The area around the standpipe, the whole graveyard, is home to abandoned ceramic pots. Some are nothing more than shards, but others have small holes in their sides. I believe them to be water jugs, left behind because they are not intact. It is easy, considering the amount of litter, to believe that these pots have simply been left behind. I decide to take one as a memento, throwing out the few dregs of water that have not leaked through the small hole at its side. Only much later do I discover that the pots are in fact funeral paraphernalia. When a Hindu dies, a pot is taken and filled with water. The pot symbolises the body, the water the soul. A small hole is made in the pot in order to let the water leave slowly, like the soul leaving a body. In symbolic terms, I have tossed someone's soul away and stolen their body.

It is too late to return the pot to the graveyard. By the time I discover my error I have already packaged it and posted it home. Posting it was a trial. I wrapped it in bubble wrap, placed it in a cardboard box that had contained a kettle, wrapped the box in plain paper. But when I arrived at the post office I was sent away – 'It is not pretty enough' I was told. Twice I returned, having rewrapped it. Each time the response was the same. I grew frustrated. The post office was little more than a small dark room. It had a single desk. There were piles of grubby papers everywhere. The walls were heavy with mould, the windows thick with sand. 'Your post office isn't pretty enough either,' I wanted to say. But by now I knew that Indian officials are pedants. There is no arguing with them. So I rewrapped the parcel, this time in the clerk's presence, under his directions. Satisfied at last, he gave me the stamps and told me to go outside. On a lopsided table beside the building stood a pot of glue that had dried to the consistency of snot. There was no brush, no stick. I had to dig my fingers into it and mash the gel onto the stamps.

A man standing in line behind me asked where I am from. When I told him South Africa he was very excited. 'Jacques Kallis!' he said, naming the recently retired star of the national cricket team. It is the same across India; as soon as people hear that I am from South Africa they want to talk to me about cricket. I know nothing about the sport, but the man was so thrilled, so kind and generous, helping me with the congealed glue, that I wanted to be able to reciprocate. I told him that a former Proteas captain, Hansie Cronje, was a relative of mine on my mother's side. At that he said, 'Oh please, let me shake your hand. Please.' He called his wife from the car, and his children. He took photos of them beside me. All the while he was smiling, returning from time to time to take my hand again. Then he became serious. 'It was terrible,' he said. 'The whole thing was a conspiracy. He was murdered. Hansie is still our hero.' I nodded, thanking him for his concern. There was nothing I could say. Despite being second cousins, I never met Hansie and I know nothing about the match-fixing scandal that ruined his cricketing career.

This part of Indian culture my father would not have liked. He found cricket to be the most boring of all sports. He would groan whenever my mother wanted to watch a game, working himself into a red-faced tirade until she went to watch in the other lounge or listen to the radio commentators in their bedroom. My father's hatred of sport stems from his relationship with his own father. In a red hardcover notebook he wrote:

> My father was mad about sport – cricket and soccer especially – and I was dragged to watch these from an early age on Saturday afternoons. I would rather have gone to the cinema. Saturdays was sport day for him. After taking us to the shops on Saturday morning we would have an early lunch and then he would go off to soccer at Hartleyvale in winter and cricket at Newlands in the summer. For a number of years he was a soccer referee and would referee games at various clubs and institutions. Later he played bowls on the weekends. Before Jean was born, if my father had some spare time on the weekend he would drive off somewhere to park on the side of the National Road where he would read the paper and then fall asleep while I read on the back seat. Time with my father taught me how to be on my own.

I wonder about this sometimes. My mother comes from a sporting family. She was an Eastern Province hurdler, a netball coach. Her father played club rugby well into his 40s. Is that one of the reasons she took so long to agree to marry my father – this man who preferred reading or listening to opera to watching sport? Juliano is sports mad. He watches anything from Formula One to volleyball. Being Brazilian, soccer is his favourite, but he is warming to cricket and rugby under my mother's tutelage. When we visit her they sit together on the sofa and she explains the rules to him. I want to laugh. I can feel my father and I sitting to the side, bored.

Yet, I see my father in Juliano in small ways. In the way he washes the dishes without complaint or fanfare. The way he tells me that I talk too much. The way he gets frustrated when I don't finish my sentences – an inheritance from my mother. The words he chooses, simple, to tell me that he is proud of me. His silences and moods. Mostly, I see my father in Juliano's legs. The strange thing is that if you lined up Juliano, my father, and my mother's father they would all look the same from behind. All three were the same sort of height. All three have the same slightly bowed legs. Watching Juliano walk is like watching my ancestry in front of me. Can you love a man more just because his legs are bowed, his height normal?

These are the things I remind myself of in the months that I am away from home. Each time I get on an aeroplane, I fit a cool girdle around my heart so that I will not miss Juliano too much. He is not a word man. His emails are brief. No more than a dozen words. Skype is challenging. I don't always have internet access where I travel, or if I do there are time differences, a bad connection, so that we spend most of the time saying 'Can you hear me? Can you hear me? What did you say? I can't hear you.' It is not that distance makes me stop loving him. It is rather that with all this time apart, with everything I am experiencing, the small things that make up a relationship can be forgotten. It is possible that some days he becomes nothing more than a name, a chore even. Each time that I return home we have to relearn what it is to share a bed. To synchronise our hunger so that we can eat together. There are the minor arguments about what to watch on television or about who finished the milk and didn't buy more. Though we are never really single, we have to relearn how to be a couple.

In the cool autumn months of Juliano's absence, I go out rarely. In the mornings I run; on weekends I run further. Otherwise I am in the flat or in my office at my mother's house. There are weeks when I have no money at all. I have to eat what I can find at my mother's or sometimes my sister's. I am unreliable. I make promises to meet friends, to go to places or events, but I back out as the dates approach. Other than lack of money, it is anxiety that keeps me from interacting with others. I am sick at the thought of conversation, of being seen and spoken to. Increasingly I am fearful of the smallest thing. Of driving to the supermarket. Of walking to the post box. Of the possibility of having to greet a neighbour or one of the security guards from the complex. I begin to snub people. I let others down. I stay away as far as possible and keep, always, to myself.

Sun is best in the corner of the flat between the sliding door to the balcony and the stairs that lead to the mezzanine floor. On colder days I stand there, warming my hands and feet, which are chilled from sitting still for too long. I watch the movement of people and cars on the main road. Across the street I notice a man leaving Vadi's Sports Bar, which used to be the Diep River Hotel. It was here that in 1924 George Scaife, my father's maternal grandfather, became the hotel manager. He had previously managed an ice-skating rink in Oudtshoorn with his brother Robert. Yet already in 1910 a postcard from a person called Popsy says that 'the rink craze is dying by degrees'. Another one from the same period records that 'a very nasty accident happened at the rink last week. A chap broke his leg hard luck to him.'

Somewhere between 1916 and 1917, George met Anna de Wet. It seems that she was reluctant, or perhaps nervous, about marrying him. The rink was losing money. What kind of future would they have?

1/2/18

Dearest Ann

Card in haste, will wright a long letter on Sunday. Very
busy as Mr North is leaving for Cape Town tomorrow.
I hope the letter you are preparing will be full of your
confidence and no nervousness for the future have a
lot to say to you when you are back have come to an
arrangement with Mr North. Yours in haste
xxxxx George xxxxx

I understand Ann's nervousness for the future, sharing it with
her. When Juliano comes home he will have no job. We will live
on whatever money I can make from editing. I don't sleep at
night. I keep the geyser off, use a candle for light. The fridge's
constant hum sings to me of the electricity it is eating, eating,
eating day and night. I am stricken – is this the life we will
have? Always apart, always poor? It is not that I question marrying Juliano. Only, what will become of us? Can we ask each
other to commit to candlelight and cold water? Can we make
this a life and not grow resentful?

Yet Ann must have been reassured by the arrangement
with Mr North, because in 1919 they were married. A year
later the rink closed and George became a barman in a hotel
in Oudtshoorn. There he stayed until 1924 when the family,
including my grandmother and her sister Peggy, moved with all
their possessions loaded onto a large lorry to Cape Town and
the Diep River Hotel. They lived in a few rooms on the second
floor, until George died in 1933, aged 51.

My grandmother didn't know for certain what had killed
her father. There had been a whisper of cancer shortly after
his death, but it was not mentioned again. Years later another
member of the family told her that George had been an alcoholic who had drunk himself to death. My grandmother had
no memory of her father drinking to excess. But she had been
young at the time of his death and her memories of him were
faint by the time alcoholism was mentioned to her.

After his death, the family had to move out of the hotel. For a time they lived with George's other brother, James, in Broad Road, Wynberg, where the three of them shared a room. George had left them nothing, and the possessions that they had filled only a few boxes. He had been a freemason for many years, so when members of George's lodge heard that the family had no money, they stepped forward to help. They rented and furnished a house at 2 Melville Road in Plumstead for the family and paid the school fees for both Trixie and Peggy. And, so that the family need not beg, they provided Ann with a monthly allowance for groceries. Even in her last years my grandmother could not free herself from a fear of running out of food, and so she hoarded tins in her cupboards, recipe books on her shelves. When she died there were items in her pantry that were more than two decades old.

It is the middle of the week, a month and a half after Juliano's departure, when I am standing in the sunny corner and become aware that I am talking. It is more than talking though. I am rehearsing conversations, reminding myself of how it might be to speak with another person. I watch my reflection in the glass of the sliding door, eyeing my facial expressions, trying to determine whether they are acceptable. I recognise that I am behaving in a way that cannot be considered normal. Below me, in the parking lot, a security guard on his rounds is watching me. I wave and step away, up the stairs, missing his response.

I make a decision, brushing my hair, changing out of track-suit pants and a hoodie for the first time in weeks. I scratch around for change, put on my sunglasses and keep my head down as I walk through the gate, past security and up to the main road before crossing to Vadi's. I am nervous. From the exterior it appears to be what people from an older generation might refer to as 'a dive'. I am not sure what it was that I was expecting, but it isn't the clean bar and tables where men in suits sit sipping beer as others in work overalls fill out betting slips. It is an anti-climax perhaps, this normalcy. Working people taking a moment out of their days to talk to friends, to watch horse-racing, rugby, anything on the numerous flatscreen televisions. I order a cheap glass of box wine at the bar and then sit at a small table, glancing at the betting forms that are on each table. A man nearby, toothless, one-legged, but polite and clean, comments that the forms are new and you need a university degree to decipher them. I laugh good-naturedly. Upstairs, the rooms where my grandmother lived have been turned into a pool hall. I can hear the clink, clink of balls hitting one another.

I always thought that George had died in one of these rooms, but when I return to *Who do you think we are?* I find that I am wrong.

> Because of the nature of his work, George and Ann could not get away together so he would take a week off work twice a year and go off on his own. It was during one of these holidays in 1933 to Fairy Glen (near Worcester) that he became ill. On his return he was rushed to Victoria Hospital where he died.

The same hospital where my grandmother died 75 years later. Was she there when her father died? She was 13 years old at the time. Would she have been allowed to see him?

There is nothing beautiful about death, about waiting for someone to die. It is frightening, ugly, boring. There are smells and sounds. Uncomfortable chairs. The last book that I remember my father reading is *Another World* by Pat Barker, an author predominantly known for her First World War fiction. When he had finished reading it, my father gave the book to me; it was interesting and different, he said. A month after his death I read it. A Somme veteran, 101 years old, is dying of stomach cancer, filled with memories and guilt from his long life. Is it in these pages that my father studied what it is to die? Did he use it to prepare himself for the pain, the lack of appetite, confusion? Perhaps that was why he urged me to read it – to train me for loss in all its grittiness.

It is true, what I read in *Another World*. The tedium of someone dying. You are told that it will be soon. But minutes pass slowly and you delay trips to the bathroom in case the person dies while you are away. 'So many people die on their own,' the nurse told my mother. 'Their family members are at work or asleep or far away. They come and say their goodbyes, and that's it. Then they leave the person to just lie there and die without anyone to be with them.'

My mother and I sat with my father most of the night before he died. It wasn't what I thought it would be. Not peaceful, not sad-but-beautiful. He screamed in pain. He kicked and flailed. Twice I ran to the nurses, 'Do something!' 'There's only so much morphine we can give him,' they replied. After some hours the screaming stopped, as did movement. Just the loud rasping breath that the doctor insisted was not painful. It is common in those who are dying, we were told.

There comes a time when like the ticking of a clock your every thought becomes die, die, die, please die. But he did not die. He lived on for hours and hours, his breath ragged and awful, just living on and on and all I could think was that he needed to die, that it was time for him to die and that I wanted to sleep.

Outside Vadi's, on the pavement, one of the homeless people who direct cars in and out of parking spaces in the car park is trying to teach his dog tricks. 'Sit,' he keeps saying, and the dog looks up at him, wagging its tail. 'Sit,' he says again. This time the dog lowers itself onto all fours and the man roars with laughter. 'Dis 'n slim brak die! Hy vat 'ie orders nie.' (This is a clever mongrel. He doesn't take orders.)

A bald man in an anorak is sitting at the neighbouring table. 'I used to live here, in the hotel,' he tells me. 'Nine rooms on this side, nine on the other,' he points at the ceiling, cutting it up with the motion of his hand. 'We were all old men, living there on our social grants. And we had no family. Then Christmas Eve 1998 they came and evicted us. Threw us all out into the parking lot with the *bergies*. Fucking landlord was bankrupt and we'd been paying rent all that time and he drank it up and we were homeless on Christmas Eve. Do you think anyone cared? Old men without family or money, and nowhere to live. Left us in the street to die and what had we done wrong? Not a fucking thing. Not one damn thing except be old and poor.'

My grandmother only told me a few stories about the time that she lived at the hotel. How they had seven dogs at the time, how she and Peggy would catch mice and put them in paper boats in the communal bath, crying when they drowned. How when she was sent to school in grade one – the same girls' school that Jean and then my sister and I went to many years later – she bit the teacher and was expelled. After that she went to the convent up on the hill in Wynberg, the school where I was teaching part-time when my father died. And finally, how she and Peggy were wearing the latest fashion – women's trousers – standing on the corner outside the hotel one day during the school holidays. At that moment a busload of nuns from the convent drove past and the girls waved at them. Upon their return to school after the holidays, her sister were called to the principal's office and reprimanded for their distasteful clothing and for having embarrassed the nuns by their trousered waving. They were given detention for an entire term. My grandmother always swore when she told this story, the polite swearing of her generation, mostly in euphemisms.

I return regularly to Vadi's in the months that I am on my own. The barmen know me by sight, getting ready a glass of red wine poured from a box, always offered with the option of ice, which I decline just as politely. 'Visiting your grandpa?' one of them always asks. 'Sit there and he will come to you,' he says and nods his head at a table in a quiet corner. He is right to a certain extent. This is where I come for comfort or when I am lonely. I come here for the history of the place, but I come too for something else: for the fact that all this life continues here. The pub is not fancy, the people are nothing special. Some of the older men dress in hats and suits, others are paint-stained or simply casual. Everyone is polite. They smile at one another. Greet one another. It comforts me to see the world existing, people living quiet lives like this, without show. Each day here is as the next. There is nothing to distinguish it from another. I am warmed by that simplicity.

But still, my anxiety persists and I continue to wake each morning with something I can only describe as dread. The behaviour, in many ways, is inherited. I recognise in my father certain patterns of behaviour that mirror mine. Waking up early, getting things done before anyone else is around. The need to stay indoors, the fear of going to new places. How he told my mother that he would never go to the cinema again. How he went always to the same restaurants. Day trips were out of the question. Even going to the supermarket was something he began to fear. Yet when people visited he charmed them, dominated the conversation, performing, delighting, so that more than one of my mother's friends was in love with this old man.

He was happiest in the garden, where, as he did with so many things, he worked without care – pulling bushes out and tossing them on the lawn, pruning the roses until nothing was left of them. Raking so hard that the grass lifted out of the earth. After his retirement he spoke every day to the postman, and to a teenage boy who had been kicked out by his parents and now lived in a shed in someone's backyard in Wittebome. Each day on his way back from work at the Pick 'n Pay, this boy came to tell my father about his day, to ask advice about his future. Most days my father gave him food or money, though I think it was the time he gave to the boy that was most valued.

There were others too. The schoolkids who came from Wittebome in the afternoon to smoke out of sight on the street corner. My father overheard them discussing a poem they had done at school that day and how they didn't understand it. So he called them over, explaining it line by line, by memory. Many afternoons they returned with questions for him, and he gave them impromptu lessons across the ranch-style fence while they smoked. He never spoke of these encounters, but I heard them from my bedroom which faced the front garden. When he came inside afterwards, his cheeks were pink. He spoke louder. His eyes shone.

This is the man he became in old age. His moods rubbed smooth as pebbles in water. All passions reduced to memories of what had passed, what might have been. A man betrayed by his body. Who went nowhere and saw few people. Who recorded in a notebook that he was prone to negativity and cynicism, listing them as facts rather than regrets. A man who wrote only once of the death he was expecting, with no more than a hint at what it was robbing him of:

As I am writing in the full knowledge that I shall not be able to travel again because time and illness are against me, I would, if it were possible, have liked to visit or see or experience the following:

1. The Trans-Siberian railways from
    Moscow to Vladivostok
2. The Great Wall of China
3. The Terracotta Army
4. The Temple at Angkor Wat
5. Aleppo in Syria
6. Persepolis and Isfahan in Iran
7. Auschwitz/Cracow in Poland
8. Tashkent and Samarkand – Silk Road

There are a few days left until Juliano's return from Harvard. I clean the flat, make a welcome home sign and the strange sponge cake that he calls the 'Benjamin Button Cake', as it tastes better the older it gets. Drawers that he left empty have filled by now, and I spend a morning clearing them out, making piles, abandoning them, returning to them, trying to find spaces for all the papers and items that I cannot bring myself to part with. There are things I could throw away – Aunty Kathleen's photos of her dead son and a gun-shaped pen that belonged to him and

175

no longer works. A note on a scrap piece of paper where, at the age of 19, I wrote that my father's taste in poetry was predictable, pedestrian. A collection of pages that my father printed off Wikipedia about what side of the road people drive on in different parts of the world. A photocopy he made of Roald Dahl's *Revolting Rhymes*. A Marmite jar from the 1950s. My father's army sewing kit. My grandmother's Girl Guide badges. A small porcelain doll that the old lady down the road gave to me when I was a child. Its face is shattered, the clothes in tatters. It is more than 100 years old, the people who loved it dead for many years. And a print-out of a letter, the font so small that I struggle to read it, folded into the pages of a book of quotes that my father kept beside his bed. I put it in my pocket as I rearrange the stockpile of my past.

'I don't know if it's age that makes the years fly by,' the letter reads, written by my father to friends in Canada at the end of 2009, 'but I just cannot believe that time can pass so quickly.'

Last year I wrote that things were a bit frantic with my retirement and all the admin of forms etc., and then my mother's death. Anyway I retired and was looking forward to a wonderful first year... However the retirement did not arrive for me. I went to the doctor for my annual check-up and he discovered a cancerous growth at the end of the colon. I was whisked off to hospital for the first operation to remove the growth and then had to spend five weeks there before the second operation to remove the temporary stoma bag and connect everything up again. The months spent getting better have been trying and frustrating. I couldn't drive a car for four months after the op, so you can imagine the daily boredom. I then slowly started to tackle little jobs like sorting through thousands of photos and getting them into order in albums. I then went onto the internet to trace the family tree which goes back to Yorkshire and Ireland. Some days I feel like a real OLD man.

This is something that I cannot imagine for Juliano and I yet. Old age, retirement, a house, a garden. Or that something darker, our eventual deaths. I can imagine only the immediate – his return. The sound of his breath in sleep. The way he will complain at the mess on the Tupperware shelf. How he won't notice that his dirty washing is cleaned and returned, folded, to his cupboard. The crumbs he will leave on the counter every morning. The way he will blow kisses at me while we watch TV, or hold my hand as we walk down the aisles of the grocery store. 'Come back to me,' I write on every day of his absence. 'I miss you,' is his reply. But still that nervousness about the future persists. What will become of us?

The last line of the letter that my father wrote is perhaps the most simple. Yet it is this sentence that reassures me and I reread it several times the night before Juliano's return: 'It's stopped raining for a bit, so I think I will head out into the garden to see how much damage the wind and rain have caused.'

ACKNOWLEDGMENTS

I would like to thank the following people and institutions for their support in writing and completing this manuscript.

Keith Jennings, Esmarie Jennings, Lize Jennings, Juliano Paccez, the Paccez family, Jean and Derek Klerck, Kobus Moolman, Arshia Sattar, Michelle Garnaut, the M-residency, Sangam House, the dancers and staff at Nrityagram, Rahul Soni, Raghu Karnad, Karthika Nair, Sally Altschuler, Mariko Nagai, Tania Rosario, Taran Kahn, Colleen Higgs, Helen Moffett, Derek Workman, Sister Chrys, St Luke's Hospice, Chennai Mathematical Institute, K.V. Subrahmanyam, Sithabile Mlotshwa, Bernadette Jansen op de Haar, Arnold Jansen op de Haar, the Africa Centre, Thamgidi Foundation, Hayley Vujcich, University of KwaZulu-Natal, National Arts Council of South Africa, Femrite, Karavan, Hilda Twongyeirwe, Birgitta Wallin, Madeleine Flack, all of my father's past pupils who wrote to me about their memories of my father, including Andre Botes and Meagan Kleinhans.

An earlier version of the vignette 'Christmas' appeared as 'Christmas in Cape Town' in the *Kalahari Review* on 12 December 2012: http://www.kalaharireview.com/nonfiction/2012/12/12/christmas-in-cape-town.html

An earlier version of the vignette 'Muzungu' appears in my short story anthology, *Away from the Dead*, published in September 2014 by Holland Park Press, UK.

An earlier and much briefer version of 'Home' appeared in *Visi* No. 72, May/June 2014.

THE AUTHOR

Karen Jennings was born in Cape Town in 1982. She has
Master's degrees in both English Literature and Creative
Writing from the University of Cape Town and a PhD in
Creative Writing at the University of KwaZulu-Natal.

Karen's stories and poetry have been published in journals
across the globe, in countries as diverse as Nigeria, Australia
and Greece. In 2010 her short story *From Dark* won the Africa
Region prize in the Commonwealth Short Story Competition.
Mia and the Shark won the English section of the Maskew
Miller Longman short story competition in 2009 and is now
studied in schools.

Her debut novel *Finding Soutbek* was published by Holland
Park Press in 2012, and was shortlisted for the inaugural
Etisalat Prize for Literature 2013. Her short story collection
Away from the Dead was published by Holland Park Press in
2014.

Karen was one of the featured authors in the South African
Sunday Times Lifestyle magazine's *The Future Fiction Edition*
to mark the 20th anniversary of South Africa's democracy.

Karen currently lives in Brazil.

More details are available from
www.hollandparkpress.co.uk/jennings

Holland Park Press is a unique publishing initiative. Its
aim is to promote poetry and literary fiction, and discover
new writers. It specializes in contemporary English fiction
and poetry, and translations of Dutch classics. It also gives
contemporary Dutch writers the opportunity to be published in
Dutch and English.

To

- Learn more about Karen Jennings
- Discover other interesting books
- Read our unique Anglo-Dutch magazine
- Find out how to submit your manuscript
- Take part in one of our competitions

Visit www.hollandparkpress.co.uk

Bookshop: http://www.hollandparkpress.co.uk/books.php

Holland Park Press in the social media:

http://www.twitter.com/HollandParkPres
http://www.facebook.com/HollandParkPress
https://www.linkedin.com/company/holland-park-press
http://www.youtube.com/user/HollandParkPress